THE SOUND OF A ROOM

What does a place sound like – and how does the sound of place affect our perceptions, experiences, and memories? *The Sound of a Room* takes a poetic and philosophical approach to exploring these questions, providing a thoughtful investigation of the sonic aesthetics of our lived environments. Moving through a series of location-based case studies, the author uses his own field recordings as the jumping-off point to consider the underlying questions of how sonic environments interact with our ideas of self, sense of creativity, and memories. Advocating an awareness born of deep listening, this book offers practical and poetic insights for researchers, practitioners, and students of sound.

Seán Street holds an Emeritus Professorship at Bournemouth University. His previous works on sound include *The Poetry of Radio* and *The Memory of Sound* (Routledge, 2013/2015) as well as a trilogy published by Palgrave, *Sound Poetics* (2017), *Sound at the Edge of Perception* (2018), and *The Sound Inside the Silence: Travels in the Sonic Imagination* (2019). He is a published poet, and a radio programme maker for the BBC and other broadcasters.

THE SOUND OF A ROOM

Memory and the Auditory Presence of Place

Seán Street

Routledge
Taylor & Francis Group

NEW YORK AND LONDON

First published 2020
by Routledge
52 Vanderbilt Avenue, New York, NY 10017

and by Routledge
2 Park Square, Milton Park, Abingdon, Oxon OX14 4RN

Routledge is an imprint of the Taylor & Francis Group, an informa business

British Library Cataloguing-in-Publication Data
A catalogue record for this book is available from the British Library

Library of Congress Cataloging-in-Publication Data
A catalog record has been requested for this book

ISBN: 978-0-367-46334-2 (hbk)
ISBN: 978-0-367-46335-9 (pbk)
ISBN: 978-1-003-02822-2 (ebk)

Typeset in Bembo
by Newgen Publishing UK

For Jo

Prophetic sounds and loud, arise forever
From us, and from all Ruin, unto the wise,
As melody from Memnon to the Sun.
We rule the hearts of mightiest men—we rule
With a despotic sway all giant minds.
We are not impotent—we pallid stones.

Edgar Allan Poe, 'The Coliseum'

CONTENTS

PREFACE

Sound haunts Place, even before and after human intervention; we are merely ghosts that resonate within it for a short time. Our earliest ancestors were alert to everything, just as an infant, or a stranger in a new place, finds every sound a potential excitement, bewilderment or terror. To enter a room of any kind is to open a door to a situation awaiting development. Whatever we contribute to the making of that development, we are joining a continuing dialogue that began before we arrived, and that will continue as a monologue after we depart. The sound of Place is indivisible in our memory from our presence in it. This book is written from a highly personal perspective, my argument being that I can only hear the sound of where I am, and since this exploration of place relies on specific examples, and also, since this is about memory, I need to acknowledge my own place as a witness within the narrative. I would ask the reader therefore to accept the presence of a certain amount of necessary autobiography in these pages; the sounds I observe in my memory and in my day-to-day life are not facts that I can claim to be at all special or in any way unique, but they are *my* heard sounds, and so things I feel I can comment upon. If this book encourages others to actively listen more to the world, then it will have served its purpose. I have been fortunate to gain from the insights of some gifted practitioners who have the capacity to make wonderful programmes and sound works, but who have been also willing and able to reflect on the philosophy of what they do, and the art of listening. Here is sound artist Colin Black reflecting on his soundscapes of Prague, Robert Bridgett in the heart of a Newfoundland storm, and Sara Jane Hall and Nathaniel Mann on a giant containership in Gdansk. Frazer Merrick listens to the sounds of a pier on the east coast of England, and poet Helen Tookey and sound recordist Martin Heslop discuss findings drawn from a potent time spent in Elizabeth Bishop's childhood home in Great Village, Nova Scotia. Sebastiane Hegarty takes us to the nuclear shingle of Dungeness, following in the steps of the film-maker Derek Jarman, while Julian May considers the sound inside a yew tree, and remembers a sonic collaboration with a Northumbrian burn. I supplement these first-hand witnesses with the texts and reflections of others: poets, philosophers and sound artists who have over time explored the sound in which they found themselves. John Cage comes immediately to mind of course, but there are others, such as Wordsworth, Merleau-Ponty and Proust, as well as contemporary theorists including Trevor Cox, Barry Truax and David Toop, all of whose thinking and writings will help open sonic windows on the world.

The power of a space re-encountered after a long absence may communicate through smell and sound; a former student wrote to me of her impression of a return visit to a teaching room we once shared in a school on the edge of the Chiltern Hills: 'First, there was the remembered scent of furniture polish, and then came gradually, the stillness that was the same as I remembered as I waited for the class to assemble, the wind against the sash windows outside.' To play a loved and lost voice, recorded in a place, within the room itself, can be overwhelming; sound travels through Time, as do we. The potency of *real time* is one of sound's most telling qualities. The most profound acoustic is held within an anechoic chamber, a space of apparently no sound, where the only thing audible is our self. It was an encounter with just such a room that unlocked much of John Cage's subsequent work and thought.

The writing of this book began in the late summer of 2019, and the final words were set down in the spring of 2020. In that time, doors began to close, and many rooms fell silent, as Covid-19 altered the sound of the world, and drove us into isolation. We all became more aware of the walls between us: personal, communal, national and global. The invisible barriers of social distancing grew over the months, and the sounds of the spaces we had taken for granted in our daily lives became memories. This journey across shared spaces grew therefore to be all the more poignant, as I revisited its staging posts through imagination and recollection, from the perspective of enforced solitude. Notwithstanding all this, however, the journey ends, as it was always intended to end, as all sentient journeys must end, in the room of the mind, as it ponders its place in the sounding world and in the broader scheme of things beyond that: the ultimate anechoic chamber of the universe, in the consideration of the room we must all enter after this.

Seán Street
Liverpool, summer 2020

ACKNOWLEDGEMENTS

This book would not have been possible without the advice, help and insights of colleagues in the professional field of sound, people who spend their lives listening to the world. I would like to thank the following for their interest and support, and for permission to quote their insights shared through discussions, interviews and correspondence: Colin Black, Rob Bridgett, Nick Buchanan, Sarah Jane Hall, Sebastiane Hegarty, Martin Heslop, Evi Karathanasopoulou, Nathaniel Mann, Julian May, Frazer Merrick, Andy and Tony Stoller, Gordon Tench and Helen Tookey. Friends and collaborators have been generous with their interest and ideas; I am pleased to thank the guitarist Neil Campbell, the composer Cecilia McDowall and the poets Hilary Davies and Jeremy Hooker for conversations that pointed to a number of avenues of thought. Also to Genevieve Aoki, my editor at Routledge, for her encouragement of the project, Bryan Biggs, director of The Bluecoat, Liverpool for opening doors, Peter Brash of the National Trust for professional ornithological advice, and Jemma Street of Liverpool University for sharing knowledge. As always, gratitude and love go to my wife Jo for her support, patience and measured, sympathetic eye, and for her painstaking reading of the draft text.

1

IN ONE CIRCLE BOUND

Room as a Sonic Event

To start with the image of a particular room: a perfect circle, the walls, three floors of books reaching up to a dome with a central skylight. Everything built on the principle of circularity. The floor area containing work tables radiating out from a central pillar, topped by an Art Deco shell-design lamp, and punctuated by free-standing bookcases. Each table seats eight people, and there are power points for computers. The sound of the room: a seemingly contradictory stillness, the sort of stillness one equates with a confined space, and yet this room is vast. It holds a silence that presses on the ears and dares sound to happen. Any sound that clings to us as we enter this huge space seems to evaporate like water. The storm of the world's noise turns back at the door; the atmosphere of the room repels it. This is the Picton Reading Room, a part of the Central Library on William Brown Street, Liverpool, England, in what is known as 'The Knowledge Quarter'. Next door on one side, up the road, is the Walker Art Gallery, while on the other, down the hill, is the World Museum. Across the cobbled street is the vast St George's Hall, below it a garden, and across a piazza to the left, a theatre. When this area was developed, in 1875, the chairman of the library and museum Sir James Picton, laid the foundation for this room, designed by Cornelius Sherlock, and modelled on the Reading Room in the British Museum in London. It was completed in 1879, and was the first electrically illuminated library in the United Kingdom.

I sit and listen to the room. It seems the right place to begin a journey into poetic acoustics, the sonic character of Place, a room full of apparent near silence that rewards concentrated attention with minute and subtle clues. It is around noon on a hot weekday in July. Although there are about eighty work stations here, today, I count only ten people sitting reading, working on laptops, or – like me – scribbling in notebooks. During term time, this place would be full of students on most days, particularly as exam time approaches. Yet the volume of occupancy does not seem to change the sonic dynamic of the place. However many people there are here at any one time, the room has the ability to absorb their sound. Likewise, because of the nature of the purpose of the space, human presence does not seem to impact greatly on sound level.

As I write these words, I am also recording on a small digital machine that accompanies me everywhere, like a camera. It will be my companion on this journey into space, and I plan to use it from time to time as I am using it today, to compare my experience with what it hears, with what places tell me of themselves as I listen to them *in situ*. Being very small, it can be unobtrusive, and I sometimes augment the built-in microphones with a lapel mic, to gain a new perspective. Because I use it all the time, I can be rather remiss in indexing the content, which means that on the memory card are hundreds of files, identified by no more than numbers. Sometimes, when I scroll through, choosing one at random, I find myself playing a sonic guessing game: where on earth is that? When did I do that? What is going on here? It is rather like browsing through a set of old photographs – I have no context, and sometimes not even a memory. A sound recording, however, is different to a snapshot; it is linear, it moves through time, and as it does so, the voice of the place gradually reminds me of where or who it is. There may be human voices, an event… but the first thing that speaks is the place itself, through its acoustics, the hard or soft surfaces, the dry exterior or the liquid space of a great church. It is better than a home movie, because in a movie I would be outside the event, looking in, observing my own experience, whereas with sound, I am reimmersed in the moment, living it again through the time it took to happen in the first place. It is that slow reveal of identification that is an essential part of the experience of a recording, setting it in the memory. It is also central to this writing.

A visual analogy might be George Perec's *An Attempt at Exhausting a Place in Paris*, experiments in observation which he carried out in Place Saint-Sulpice in October 1974. Perec's book has fascinated me for some years, printing as it does the being of an overcast Parisian day in 1974 onto time: the everyday, the humdrum, what happens when nothing happens. Sitting behind a café window, Perec wrote what he saw, *exactly*, with forensic attention to detail. Much of the space in which he worked through that weekend may be taken in casually and quickly, almost at a glance. 'A great number', wrote Perec,

> if not the majority, of these things have been described, inventoried, photographed, talked about, or registered. My intention… was to describe the rest instead: that which is generally not taken note of, that which is not noticed, that which has no importance: what happens when nothing happens other than the weather, people, cars, and clouds.

(Perec, p. 3)

To live in the moment like this is to develop an acute sense of being alive, and there can be no more laudable intention for any writer at the start of a quest than to invoke such an aim. Eyes and ears work in partnership, as we shall see and hear. Active listening is a learned skill as well as for some, an inborn instinct. It is to be nurtured, and the rewards can be like switching on a hearing aid to a deaf person. See what was there all the time!? I want to train my ears and mind to *listen* in the same way Perec *looked*. A key part of my study will be an invitation to the colleagues in radio and sound recording to reflect on their work, and share their thoughts and memories on the role of an acoustical space as an active partner and participant. This direct witness will partner my own. I want to ask: why does the place sound like this? What has shaped it towards this sonic character? What is its effect on us when we enter it? How does active listening change our perception of where we are?

For the purpose of this study, a room is more than an inhabited physical space, it is a field of consciousness, a sonic energy field with ourselves at its centre. This writing is about missed sounds, but it is also an investigation into how sounds govern our sense of place, how we contribute to them and how they partner us in terms of perception, image and the sound of ourselves. A field, a park or a sea shore is thus a room, as much as the library in which I am writing now. Central to the aural character of where we are at any single moment is how a space changes the seed of a sound through reverberation and resonance, as the reed of an oboe is changed by the body of the instrument into which it sings. Linda-Ruth Salter takes us back to first principles in summary:

> Sound is caused by a vibration in air that propagates in the form of aud-ible mechanical waves of pressure and displacement. When these waves pass through air in an enclosed space, they reflect off the surfaces of the enclosed space. These surfaces include not only the six surfaces of a typical rectangular enclosure, but also the surfaces of whatever is in that enclosure, including objects and people. In a non-enclosed space, these waves reflect off the phys-ical elements in the space, including trees, people, hills, water, and so on. Each type and shape of reflective surface absorbs, reflects and diffuses sound waves in different ways. The human ear hears, and the human mind decodes the differences, determining whether the space is open or enclosed; the volume of the enclosure; the materials of the enclosure; the number, materials, and shapes of the contents; and the placement and direction of objects and reflective surfaces in the space. We can "read" a space with our ears.
>
> *(Salter, pp. 776–7)*

The worlds that this book seeks to explore are wide-ranging, from our daily places – our domestic rooms, car spaces and public transport, to the houses of the sacred, performance halls and the strange twilight environments of archaeoacoustics. These are the physical realities of the sound of rooms in all their principal manifestations. Yet this writing also seeks to explore certain *non*-physical sonic rooms, spaces where sound creates its own spaces within the mind and the memory, the sound rooms we enter when we listen to music, or hear a radio play, or even occupy the sonic space within a poem. We are ourselves, rooms of sound, alone in the crowd as we stand in the arena, absorbed in a favourite band, or at the cinema, enveloped in surround sound, while at the same moment, we each experience our own version of the experience we are hearing, according to where we are sitting or standing within the room, and according to preference. Some may find the movie sound too loud; others may not even notice the volume. How our personal room is tuned, dictates what our sonic preferences may be. We inhabit communal sound, but we digest it on a personal basis. Barry Truax refers to the 'acoustic community':

> The *acoustic community* may be defined as any soundscape in which acoustic information plays a pervasive role in the lives of the inhabitants... Therefore, the boundary of the community is arbitrary and may be as small as a room of people, a home or building, or as large as an urban community, a broadcast area, or any other system of electroacoustic communication. In short, it is any system within which acoustic information is exchanged.
>
> *(Truax, p. 58)*

Subsequent chapters will particularise the sounds of environments that surround us as we live; we cannot avoid being *somewhere*. At various steps, the transcription of recorded sound will bring us back to the character of the place, its voice and the fact that it is at one and the same time a constructed thing and an ongoing and subtly changing sounding-board and echo-chamber. Sonic horizons can be seductive; the immediacy of a place may draw our attention from the context within which the place itself exists. Walking into my book-lined dining room, I am aware of a changing ambience, different from the hall outside. Yet my recorder reminds me that outside *this* room, is the room of the street on which this house is situated; it changes as the day changes – early morning stillness, birdsong into rush hour traffic, and so on through the stations of the day. It is a room within a room, and at the centre is me, with my microphone. We live in series, and a room does not require walls to enclose us.

At the heart of this is a mystery. The Swiss architect Peter Zumthor wrote:

> Imagine extracting all foreign sound from a building... imagine what it would be like with nothing left, nothing there to touch anything else. The question arises: does the building still have a sound?... I think each one emits a kind of tone. They have sounds that aren't caused by friction. I've no idea what they are. Maybe it's the wind or something. But you only really feel there's something else there when you enter a space that's soundproofed.
>
> *(Zumthor, p. 31)*

I am comforted to know that an architect of Zumthor's standing also senses the inherent characteristic voices of spaces, but cannot define them. Like him, I would place the sound of apparently empty space at the beginning of all things: 'Listen! Interiors are like large instruments, collecting sound, amplifying it, transmitting it elsewhere' (ibid., p. 29). What matters most of all in the unravelling of this is not that it occurs, but that we should be aware of it. By invoking the works of another great architect, we begin to understand that our ability to listen, so long taken for granted, is vital to our placement in the world, placing us always at the very hub of everything that makes up our experience. Juhani Pallasmaa has suggested:

> Sight isolates, whereas sound incorporates; vision is directional, whereas sound is omni-directional. The sense of sight implies exteriority, but sound creates an experience of interiority. I regard an object, but sound approaches me; the eye reaches, but the ear receives. Buildings do not react to our gaze, but they do return sounds back to our ears… It is thought-provoking that the mental loss of the sense of centre in the contemporary world could be attributed, at least in part, to the disappearance of the integrity of the audible world.
>
> *(Pallasmaa, p. 53)*

In the twenty-first century, certain words have been reappropriated with fresh nuances of meaning; among these words are 'wireless' (formerly an archaic generic term for radio transmission, or actually a noun for the object of reception itself, and sometimes both. For instance, we listen to *wireless* transmissions on a *wireless*). Similarly, the word 'stream' has become familiar as a term denoting the continuous act of transmitting or receiving through the internet a programme or other electro-acoustic communication. When Albert Bregman wrote his seminal book *Auditory Scene Analysis* in 1990, he employed 'stream' as a word to demonstrate the multiplicity of sonic information we are open to absorbing at any one time:

> A physical happening (and correspondingly its mental representation) can incorporate more than one sound, just as a visual object can have more than one region. A series of footsteps, for instance, can form a single experienced event, despite the fact that each footstep is a separate sound. A soprano singing with piano accompaniment is also hear as a coherent happening, despite being composed of distinct sounds (notes). Furthermore, the singer and piano together form a perceptual entity – the "performance" – that is distinct from other sounds that are occurring. Therefore, our mental representations of acoustic events can be multifold in a way that the mere word "sound" does not suggest.
>
> *(Bregman, p. 10)*

Bregman also reserves the word 'stream' for a perceptual representation, with the physical cause described by the phrase 'acoustic event' or the word 'sound' (ibid.).

While acknowledging both the elegance and logic of this thinking, I am seeking here to focus on a prevailing ambience within a place itself, so would wish to employ Bregman's 'stream' as an implicit term rather than becoming embroiled in a confusion of changing meaning due to the passage of time and changes in technological vocabulary.

To return to the here and now, the sound of the library is as much a stream of consciousness as a stream of auditory evidence. In today's room, the actual fabric of the walls is for the most part assumed, obscured as it is by books, fifteen layers of bookshelves following the circumference of the architecture. Silence. And yet as I look up and round, attempting – and failing before I start – to estimate the sheer number of volumes that surround me, I gain the sense of a place that through the projection of the imagination may in fact be one of the noisiest rooms I have ever sat in. Every book has a voice, the expression of the thoughts of its author, with the potential for speaking directly to me. These truly are whispering galleries, and cumulatively, the whispers are deafening. It is also a room of murmuring ghosts, a chamber where past and present touch, because where I sit, generations before me have sat: academics, poets, students, revolutionaries and local people who simply wanted to look at the day's papers, to find a place away from the worries of life and to make sense of it all. There is a fellowship held in this circular space, a companionable presence across time. Who knows what other journeys began here? In the process of researching this book, one of my favourite statements came from the composer, musician and sound artist Nathaniel Mann:

> For me there is an endless pleasure to be found in deducing just how 'a thing might ring,' and in knowing that there might be something about the way each object or structure was built, assembled, formed, wrought, grown or even broken that lets it have a second (secret) life, as a sound making instrument.[1]

To my ears – and I suspect, to Nathan's – that might equally be a hollowed-out stone or the Taj Mahal.

I continue to listen. Silence here of course is a relative thing, like a visual interpretation of white; Wittgenstein gives us the analogy:

> If I say a piece of paper is pure white and then place snow next to it and it appears grey, in normal surroundings and for ordinary purposes I would call it white and not light grey. It could be that I'd use a different and, in a certain sense, more refined concept of white in, say a laboratory, (where I sometimes also use a more refined concept of 'precise' determination of time).
> *(Wittgenstein, p. 38)*

The relativity of silence may thus be seen as a bedrock for the canvas it represents to highlight the minutiae of sounds that evolve out of it or intrude into it. It is the uniformity of it that renders the small scraps of sound that inhabit it, as important. Someone unpacks a bag, there's the buzz of a zip, the brief rip of Velcro, the scratching of a pen, the tapping of fingers on a keyboard from the woman sitting next to me, I hear someone nearby breathing. A low rumble from somewhere beneath my feet confuses me for a moment, but then I remember that Liverpool's urban rail system runs through tunnels directly beneath this complex of buildings. It passes, and then, as if in answer, there is the faint drone of a light aircraft over-head, just for a few moments, before it too fades. I blow my nose (the pollen count is high today across the sweltering city). A woman I cannot see on the other side of the room sneezes and a man somewhere else coughs. It is as though the circularity of the space we share invites a kind of subconscious responsive communication, but this is pure fancy on my part. There are moments between movements in a symphony concert, when, as audience members, we echo one another with a cough, a clearing of the throat, or a shuffle in the seat. A room is always ready to share the sounds of its inhabitants, but right now it resumes the sense of itself, and study continues.

These things form the theme of the journey this book seeks to take from this point onwards, a journey of listening to space, of interrogating the rooms in which we find ourselves, with or without walls, and exploring the way Place duets and interacts with us sonically. Because we cannot survive a vacuum, sound is every-where. We make it and we live in it and with it, even when it is as subtle as the Picton is right now. To 'break the silence': I dwell on the meaning of the phrase. There are indeed rooms such as this one that seem to actually *make* silence, so that to interrupt it with a sound is literally to break it as one might break a stick in two with one's hands. Every space has its default sound as Zumthor and Pallasmaa suggest, to which we contribute simply by our presence in it. But the auditory personality of the place was there before we arrived, and it will be there after we leave, waiting for someone else to change it with *their* presence. To take, as it were, 'sound photographs' – to listen to the everyday and hear how extraordinary it is – to appreciate the moment as one may examine an old daguerreotype, say, of a street scene from the past in which nothing of particular note seems to be going on, just ordinary life happening: these are the moments to be savoured, when we come closest to shaking hands with time, and hearing the past. I look at the clock. I have been listening, writing and recording for thirty-five minutes. It is time now to leave, to go home and to hear what my recorder has been hearing all this time. I switch it off. The tiny click of the button I press breaks into the Picton Room's presence.

'In the Sound, a Thought'

Five days have gone by since I sat and listened to the Picton Room. Now, back at my home desk, and reflecting on the experience while preparing to listen to my recording, I wrestle with a number of complications. Listening to a recording of a place or event out of the context of the place itself, is quite a different thing to listening *in situ*; being present in a place, a person with unimpaired visual and audio faculties interprets the world through a combination of those senses. Thus, I hear a noise and turn to seek the source. Once satisfied, I return to my work. A man on an upper gallery of the Picton Library drops a book, and a micro-second later my ear hears the book's impact on the floor: I look up: cause and effect. On the other hand, an audio playback of the scene, especially when listened to after the passing of time, requires memory to contextualise, as Abraham Moles has written:

> With visual perception, the eye goes where it wants… As for the sound-scape, it is imposed on us via a sequential system: its distinctive components are stuck in a specific order onto the length of the track, and we can do nothing about this – we are subject to this order – and the advent of new components entails the loss of old ones that can but shine for a brief moment in the phosphorescence of our working memory. On account of this, our ability to hierarchize such memory is affected.
>
> *(Moles, quoted in Chion, p. 138)*

In other words, we may become over-reliant on the very technology we have used as an aide memoire, to the extent that it obliterates aspects of the original sonic memory. This is increasingly a part of modern life for a generation that uses online sources to gather information. Our minds are changing, so that we retain only what we need to hold; the facts and details that cannot be gleaned from any other source: the rest, we know we can 'Google', so the brain makes no attempt to retain it. Once I start to play my recording, part of my mind relaxes, safe in the knowledge that the amorphous flow of time and event has been 'fixed' and solidified. Memory loses its edge. There's a procedural health warning here: it would seem that my sound recording will not replace my note-taking. There are gains and losses to be had, but it is important from the start to clarify what these are. As Chion says, a recording 'decontextualises sound', while at the same time, it changes spontaneity 'by making an object repeatable… These two listening positions – the "in situ" and the "via recording" – are thus fundamentally different, and they condition perception in likewise different ways' (Chion, p. 139). Implicitly, my back-up recording seems to reduce the sound to a sample in a 'study method' and 'lab report'. Chion challenges this idea. It is something else entirely: it is the very condition of the study of sound, but a condition that changes sound's very essence. *In situ* listening is characterised by a selection – be it reflexive or conscious – of relevant components and the repression of others, which remain unconsciously 'heard' (ibid.).

This gives me permission to continue with my methods, with the proviso that my immediate impressions of a soundscape in note form, are an essential part of the mix – in every sense of the word. Thus armed, I consider how I will define the 'rooms' I want to visit. This is the place to take stock of intentions. The Picton Reading Room has been a good starting point, but I want also to think about spaces in which personal privacy and shared occupancy affect how we respond and what we listen for: in other words, (for example) private and public transport. Driving is a very personal thing: I open the car and get in, there is ritual to it. Seat belt, ignition key, engine, and the in-car entertainment. I cannot take notes while driving, so I rely here very much on memory, human and digital. The recorder tells me of the subtle sounds I hear but never notice. The clicking of the indicators, the murmuring of the gears, the creaking of the fabric, and me – I had no idea I cleared my throat so many times. It is a nervous habit. There is a low bass rumble I have never noticed. When the radio or the music system is playing, I do not hear these things. Likewise, I never remember the journey to work, partly because I do it so often, and partly because part of my attention is usually on the news or the music. So how do I do this? In my imagination, this metal box is moving me now through unfamiliar landscapes. The car is climbing, we are on a North Welsh mountainside, travelling up and away from a broad bay at our backs. I can see the place has become widescreen, but I observe it through the television of the car window, and the box that moves me through this spectacular terrain feels and sounds claustrophobic, separates me from the sound of the place. The indicator clicks as I park. The door opens, and the mountainside floods in like water. A new soundscape begins. We will return both to inner and outer spaces of travel later in the book. The rooms of landscape will be a particularly interesting area to explore. These are not empty spaces, but inherently dynamic. An environment imbued with its own natural characteristics can work with imagination or memory, and certainly with mood, to create a sense of place that is unique and lasting. One room can evoke another in the mind, full of association, picking up our own prevailing mood, and enhancing it, agreeing with it, in sympathy. Take Matthew Arnold's famous poem 'Dover Beach', for example:

> Listen! You hear the grating roar
> Of pebbles which the waves draw back, and fling,
> At their return, up the high strand,
> Begin, and cease, and then again begin,
> With tremulous cadence slow, and bring
> The eternal note of sadness in.

The melancholy is in Arnold's mood, but here it becomes positively tidal, mirrored by the terrain, deposited afresh with each wave that breaks on the shore. Then the associations begin; every shore is linked by sea, and time and place come together in his mind as he remembers:

> Sophocles long ago
> Heard it on the Aegean, and it brought
> Into his mind the turbid ebb and flow
> Of human misery; we

> Find also in the sound a thought,
> Hearing it by this distant northern sea.
> *(Arnold, p. 144)*

The associations become personal as the reader is prompted by the thought to evoke mental images of their own shorelines, the sounds of coastal rooms and the lapping, brush or crash of waves of remembered shores, and the metaphors that come with them. Sea shores above many other forms of landscape show us that there are species of Place, and within those species, localities, regions and cultures shaped from evolution and circumstance. To return to the personal soundscape of our car-domain, and the rooms in which we travel through the world; when these become a shared space, we enter into a democracy that can be challenging. A concert hall or a sports stadium is a room in which we participate in experience and share not only the audio of it, but also our own physical and sonic perspective of the event. The rooms we inhabit move as we move, and their location can be fluid; our seat on the train may be part of a space shared with companions, or it may be a place of sought solitude. There is a tension between the requirements of our personal sound world and communal environments. Around us there are the defining sounds of the train, bus or aircraft that provide the envelope of the acoustic event that psychologically contextualises our experience. My recording device reminds me that the train room I rent for the duration of the journey holds me in a static present as it moves through time and space. My auditory experience of its presence around me lodges in memory as the journey itself, rather than as the medium through which the journey is encountered, because the sound and temperature of the landscape through which I pass is denied to me, cocooned as I am within the metal canisters of modern travel. All the more traumatic, given the brutal places of transit (stations and airline terminals) through which I must pass to earn the right to own membership of these mobile clubs.

How wide a landscape can be in sound terms, even in the suburbs of a city. From my back garden, I can hear the sounds of shipyards and the container port on the River Mersey. Our sonic horizon is frequently further and wider than our visual fences. It offers us a psychological sense of space and perspective that opens consciousness. On the other hand, those horizons have the capacity to reverse. In the city centre on a Friday or a Saturday night, I can see right down to the bottom of the street, but I can only hear for a few yards, hemmed in as I am by urban noise: music, laughter, shouting and singing. It feels limiting, mind-numbing, claustrophobic and sometimes threatening. It can also be life-affirming. These are shared places with one another, but also with the past. As we listen back to our recordings, we should imaginatively hear the ghosts that once inhabited the very same space, whispering to us.

I return my mind to the library, a cloistered room padded with books and carpet. A similar space built of stone and marble would ring like a bell. Many buildings around the world have been constructed with the specific imaginative intention of creating often deliberately spectacular sonic effects, just as their art has sometimes told graphic and salutary stories in order to subjugate and elevate their faithful visitors. The Venetian churches of Palladio and others were designed with minute attention to their sound characteristics, and the music composed to be played and sung in them cannot communicate in the same way when heard in spaces where these sonorities are not considered. It was Goethe who wrote, 'I call architecture "petrified music"' (Howard and Moretti, p. 8).

A song may be background noise, obtrusive sonic rabble, or an immersive acoustic room of its own making, in which we disappear for three minutes or several hours, and perhaps emerge altered, just as a poem is a room made of printed or handwritten shapes signifying sound and surrounded by white walls that cannot contain it. Absorbing sound becomes an increasingly personal business; we listen to our chosen sound tracks, be they speech or music, as we move around the world, visually taking in places that may be dramatic juxtapositions of the audio images we are feeding ourselves. The use of earbuds places the sound inside the body, and the ears thus become doorways and windows into the room of self where our own music happens. In the end, it is *all* music; headphones that utilise the bone of our skull to conduct sound, rather than the ear canal, may be less immersive, but some may prefer to have the option of having both the inner room and the consciousness of the environmental context through which we experience the sound (as in a live performance) at the same time. These pages have a number of reflections on music because it provides its own mental and emotional rooms. It is also the most potent awakener of a physical room's sonic characteristics, as it works in partnership with a space to aurally colour the air.

The Shape of a Sound

After the passage of several days, I finally settle down with my Picton recording and a pair of headphones, to immerse myself in the sounds of which my machine and I shared witness. The first thing I notice in spite of the insulation of the place, is a more 'liquid' resonance than I remember. It affects all sounds in a way that I had not registered *in situ*. Every sound has a tiny echo, and there is the sense of an environment that is largely composed of wood. Somewhere there is an occasional 'beep' that I do not remember, but which I think must be emanating from a computer in the lobby outside. Although the doors to the main library remain open, it is surprising how little sound enters. It really is as though the fabric of the place dissolves sound whenever it tries to intrude from outside. There is the 'beep' again, faint, distant, from another world. Between these sound events there is atmosphere, a feeling of a large space. There must be air conditioning in the room, but if so, it is very subtle. Mostly, the place seems to simply breathe. There is also an indefinable perspective that gives me something of the scale; in the foreground, I hear a faint scratching from my pen, and the occasional page turn of my notebook. The most interesting aspect of listening after five days, to the recording is its mnemonic value. Hearing a tiny sound, the unzipping of a case on the other side of the room, or a cough, I am given my memory of the room like a photograph; I can see the spines of books on the galleries, and I am transported back to my seat at the workstation, and the exact visual aspect of where I had chosen to sit that day. Memory and imagination are, I realise, playing a key part in this exercise. There is also the separate sensation of objective listening. To some extent I am able to divorce myself from the moment, and hear the room, as it were, at a distance. I had not expected such a sense of drama in this recording of *almost* nothing; there is a tension in the sound, that was not present in the actual experience; the listener cannot help but stay tuned, for what happens next, and there IS a sense that something is about to happen. Here, now, I have only my ears, my imagination and my mind's memory; at the time the recording was made, I was sitting beside my machine, all my senses absorbing the experience. As a listener, the thirty-five minutes' duration of the recording passes sooner than I would have expected; I had not anticipated to be so riveted by such minimalism! I hear my hand brush the machine, and the slight click of the 'off' switch, and then the contrast between recorded presence and a pure sonic vacuum as my headphones suddenly find nothing speaking to them.

My recording of the Picton Reading Room, made on Friday 26 July 2019, between 12.35 and 13.10, holds the fixed sounds of that place and that time, within the limitations of my recording device. Had I been more ambitious, I could have set up a complex series of microphones to do justice to the shape and size of the room, and I should be playing that back now in surround sound. That however would defeat the purpose of this particular exercise: the immediacy of the experience. I would like simply to remember being there, and to have the means of being reminded of that. If I returned, I would find the room much as it was on that day; the people will no doubt be different, more or less of them occupying their workstations. Otherwise, it will look the same, the same books in the same places on the same shelves, and above all, the same shape and graceful architecture. Indeed, in Chapter 8, this book will near the end of its journey in the same place, so there will be an opportunity to test that premise. Now something else occurs to me; it is all very well, me listening to sounds of a place with which I am familiar, in hindsight; but how much would this recording mean or convey to someone with no prior knowledge of the place, and no information other than the sound, to guide them? There is a layer to this exploration that needs to be unpicked, and I ask my friend Nick Buchanan to listen to a copy, 'blind', without information or clues. Nick is a writer, a Psychotherapeutic Counsellor and Clinical Hypnotherapist, as well as a Master Practitioner in Neuro-Linguistic Programming, so I trust his ability to listen actively and sympathetically. I send him the audio file; his response to the recording is interesting:

> At first I thought this must be some area which concerns itself with the
> passing of time – a waiting area perhaps… then I thought it was too quiet

for that. The space has an echo – so it must be big enough for such – like an atrium. Then I heard pages turning and footsteps but no voices. The air seemed dense with concentration or focus. The sound of a book closing. Someone sneezes, but no one responds with a 'bless you.' It is a place where no one talks. That gave me a Library perhaps?[2]

So the nature of the space communicates itself to the 'innocent ear'. Nick picked up the echo, which on my own second play-through is clear to hear; why did I not notice this at the time? Our senses interact, but they also subvert one another. A beautiful building or room can be seductive; we are like a child in a sweet shop, drawn by all kinds of sensations that often prevent us from focusing on one single point of concentration. It is hard to be objective, detached and analytical, particularly on first meeting a place, and although I have been in the Picton many times, I am always so struck by the beauty, symmetry and perfect visual balance of the place that I sometimes almost forget what I came for. I should have closed my eyes. Most significant of all in Nick's reaction however is this: 'The air seemed dense with concentration or focus'. That a room's 'presence' can be communicated to an objective listener through listening alone is deeply important to this exploration of the sound that surrounds us, and in this instance demonstrates a working relationship, a partnership with the spaces we inhabit which in turn creates a kind of joint personality that occupies the air and is actually *audible*. Goethe may have referred to architecture as 'petrified music', but the sound of a place, the temporal music within it, is flowing, ever-changing and above all interactive. 'Soundscapes are alive by definition; they can never be static' (Blesser and Salter, p. 15). There is then, a dynamic at work, a movement, of air, that is carrying sound, and it is the way the space interacts with it, that defines where we are. Blesser and Salter put it beautifully:

> On the one hand, just as light sources are required to illuminate visual architecture, so sound sources (sonic events) are required to "illuminate" aural architecture in order to make it aurally perceptible... By responding to human presence, aural architecture is dynamic, reactive and enveloping. In contrast, because human beings do not possess an intrinsic means for generating light, a space does not react to our visual presence, which manifests itself there only through interrupted or reflected light – as shadows or mirror images.
>
> *(Ibid.)*

In other words, we may sit as long as we like in a completely darkened room; although our eyes may to some extent adjust, the visual architecture of the place will not manifest itself of its own volition, it will not interact with us. If we whisper or sing or shout however, the room responds, and offers us information about its size, shape and even contents. This sense of a relationship between us and where we are at any given moment is both extremely moving, and also at the heart of this current study. John Hull, a writer and academic who became blind, and who powerfully described his sonic realignment with the world in his book *Touching the Rock*, wrote: 'If only rain could fall inside a room, it would help me to understand where things are in that room, to give a sense of being in the room, instead of just sitting on a chair' (Hull, p. 27). Perhaps we need to take a step back, pick up the dictionary, turn to semantics and define our terms.

Firstly, sound; my *Shorter OED* offers me nearly a page of variations on the word, and across that range, certain definitions stand out:

> The sensation produced in the organs of hearing when the surrounding air is set in vibration in such a way as to affect these; also, that which is or may be heard; the external object of audition, or the property of bodies by which this is produced.

It is good to be reminded of fundamentals. But 'sound' is a complex word, with nuances of meaning. As a verb, for example, 'to cause to make a sound, to blow, to strike or play [on an instrument]', 'to utter in an audible tone… to celebrate'. I like the idea of sound as a 'celebration'. In another sense, an object or structure may be deemed 'sound' by tapping its surface, and listening to changes in tone. A theory or a person may be considered 'sound' if they withstand scrutiny. Then again, it can mean 'to sink in, penetrate, pierce… to measure, or ascertain, to investigate'. At the other extreme of course, at least on the face of it, there is the thing we call 'silence: the state or condition when nothing is audible; complete quietness or stillness; noiselessness'. Several times on this journey I shall debate in various ways whether or not this state can actually exist outside of a vacuum. One of my favourite linguistic coincidences in English is that the word 'silent' is an anagram of 'listen'. But I should also interrogate another word in that definition, 'stillness: absence of movement or physical disturbance, motionlessness; freedom from agitation, tranquillity; freedom from turbulence or self assertion'. Later in this book we shall explore the sound of sacred spaces, and at the heart of many faiths is this kind of stasis. There is something else though, something in a room that may lie between these poles; I turn the dictionary pages back to 'A' and look at 'ambience: circling about; surrounding, encompassing… especially as a fluid'. This is haunting, a feeling of a pre-existing state, containing – perhaps – its own sonic being, which leads me to 'presence: a sense of the place or space in front of a person, or which immediately surrounds him [or her]'.

Here is something close to my purpose: an atmosphere through which I move, a canvas, seemingly blank, but possessing its own base colour and texture, even if that colour is white and that texture is as smooth and cold as marble. Sound becomes like liquid. I find myself thinking of the idea of that mysterious substance *aether* or ether, a material that according to ancient thought, and even into the twentieth century, was thought by some scientists to fill the universe, permeating the space between stars and planets; it was a concept that had been used in several theories to explain certain natural phenomena, such as light and gravity. For early radio pioneers, ether was a term in regular usage, a part of the vocabulary of the medium for transmitted sound. While the sound of ether may not be what I'm listening to, the *ambience*, the *presence* I am seeking to identify in this book does seem to have some of those flowing, amorphous qualities. It is the sound of the world happening around us, nothing less.

Why should it matter that I acknowledge this? Is there any value in observing and acknowledging the different sonic characters of various spaces? Given that I am inevitably always IN a space of some sort, I must respond by answering that to recognise the audibility of an environment is to record my presence within it, and therefore to show posterity a sound moment from my time that was witness to the ongoing song of various places within the personal sphere of a single lived experience in the first third of the twenty-first century. R. Murray Schafer writes of what he calls *keynote sounds* as:

> …those which are heard by a particular society continuously or frequently enough to form a background against which other sounds are perceived. Examples might be the sound of the sea for a maritime community or the sound of the internal combustion engine in the modern city. Often keynote sounds are not consciously perceived, but they act as conditioning agents in the perception of other sound signals.
>
> *(Schafer, p. 272)*

In some of my previous writings, I have sought to drill down through this soup of sound, to find within it the individual clues to the sometimes minute but meaningful things going on within it. In this study, I want to focus on the soup itself, to listen without taking anything for granted. It is not easy, because as I have already experienced here, we condition ourselves so well to our environment. As Schafer says, we learn to shut out surrounding sound, and work within it. I suffer from tinnitus, a more or less continuous whistling in my ears, and I have adapted my listening in such a way that – most of the time – I do not notice it. (Asking questions of stillness, as in the Picton Room, becomes more of a challenge in this respect; suddenly that whistling inside my head forces itself to the fore, but that is my own personal room's keynote sound that I live with all day and every day.) For the most part, scotomisation has been a growing requirement in the human species as the world's soundscape has become more intrusive and ubiquitous. We have learnt to employ increasingly 'the cocktail party effect'; when locked in conversation at a noisy gathering, we may choose to focus on our conversant, or, if he or she is not holding our attention, we may choose to retune to the fascin-ating, perhaps salacious gossip coming from someone behind us, or elsewhere in the room. Our listening faculties – or rather our mental filters – possess intensely selective mechanisms that channel the most important, relevant or interesting material, and sift out the rest, turning it into ambient noise. We are at our roots then, it seems wireless coherers, moving along the radio dial until we find the station that's relevant to our taste. This is where a recorder comes in useful. The ear works with the brain, but the recorder has no brain, no selective process; it fixes the sonic moment as well as its technology allows. In the earliest days of recording, at the time when Eiffel, Edison and others made the first recordings in the mid to late nineteenth century, the voice was everything. The phonograph was perceived as a dictation machine, and the business model was clear. Sound as art, the audible witness of life as it happened, was not on the agenda. Chion reminds us:

> The acoustic world of the time – the world of vehicles and machines – was neglected. It was however during this same era of the end of the nineteenth and first couple of decades or so of the twentieth century that the sounds of the horse-drawn carriages coexisted with – added little by little – trams, steam trains, subways, and automobiles, which would have perhaps granted the "urban symphony" an ideal acoustic variety (the combination of discontinuous and continuous sounds) that it has since lost.
>
> *(Chion, p. 132)*

In listening to the presence around us, we shall acknowledge existence, and our place within it, if only for the here and now. When I leave a space, my consciousness, my awareness of the sound of that place moves into memory, but the place continues, with its own acoustic poetry, layered down successively, more and more subtle until the base note, the foundation of the blank canvas. Answering the question 'can silence be heard?', Schafer's answer was

> yes, if we could extend our consciousness outward to the universe and to eternity, we could hear silence. Through the practice of contemplation, little by little, the muscles and the mind relax and the whole body opens out to become an ear.
>
> *(Schafer, p. 262)*

This is not a quest for silence, although sometimes, as here in this reading room, we may come close to asking a question of it, while at others there will be circumstances when the presence of a room will suggest it. Moreover, we are searching for the ability to listen purely, actively and attentively, to understand what it is that spirals down through our ears into our brain, creating a unique partnership between ourselves and where we are, as a contributory part of that presence. It is appropriate that we begin in a circular room, because it is itself, in its very shape, a metaphor for the field of consciousness, the circle of awareness, that is our personal room, moving with us wherever we go, with our own individual being always at its centre. Gaston Bachelard wrote that 'for a dreamer of words, what calm there is in the word round. How peacefully it makes one's mouth, lips and the being of breath... Being is round' (Bachelard, p. 239). In his hymn of praise to the (then) new science and art of radio, commissioned by John Reith of the BBC to mark the opening of the giant Daventry transmitting station in 1925, the poet Alfred Noyes wrote:

> All are in one circle bound,
> And all that ever was lost is found.
>   *(Noyes, in Street, p. 21)*

The circle holds the significance of sound and transmits it. A whispering gallery sends murmurs around its walls, but purpose and intention in a place may also archive in memory as well as 'broadcast' itself, a quality to which we respond, and through our presence, develop. Listening actively and attentively is to press a switch in the mind that opens lines of communication which are in fact always 'live' although mostly unacknowledged. We are always hearing, but we properly attend to what we hear for a fraction of our time on earth. The point of departure for this journey may have been 'dense with concentration and focus', but it is time to pack notebook, pen and recorder, open the door, and head off to listen to the world beyond these walls.

Notes

1 Nathaniel Mann, personal communication with the author, reproduced with permission.
2 Nick Buchanan, personal communication with the author.

References

Arnold, Matthew. Ed. John Bryson. *Poetry and Prose*. London: Rupert Hart-Davis, 1954.
Bachelard, Gaston. *The Poetics of Space*. Boston, MA: Beacon Press, 1994.
Blesser, Barry and Salter, Linda-Ruth. *Spaces Speak, Are You Listening?* Cambridge, MA: MIT Press, 2007.
Bregman, Albert S. *Auditory Scene Analysis: the Perceptual Organisation of Sound*. Cambridge, MA: MIT Press, 1994.
Chion, Michel. Trans. James A. Steintrager. *Sound: an Acoulogical Treatise*. Durham, NC: Duke University Press, 2016.
Howard, Deborah and Moretti, Laura. *Sound and Space in Renaissance Venice*. New Haven, CT: Yale University Press, 2009.
Hull, John. *Touching the Rock*. London: SPCK, 1990.
Pallasmaa, Juhani. *The Eyes of the Skin: Architecture and the Senses*. Chichester: Wiley, 2012.
Perec, George. Trans. Marc Lowenthal. *An Attempt at Exhausting a Place in Paris*. Cambridge, MA: Wakefield Press, 2010.

Salter, Linda-Ruth. 'What You Hear is Where You Are', in Mark Grimshaw-Aagaard, Mags Walther-Hansen and Martin Knakkergaard (eds) *The Oxford Handbook of Sound and Imagination*. Oxford: Oxford University Press, 2019, pp. 765–87.

Schafer, R. Murray. *The Soundscape*. Rochester, VT: Destiny Books, 1994.

Street, Seán. *Radio Waves: Poems Celebrating the Wireless*. London: Enitharmon Press, 2004.

Truax, Barry. *Acoustic Communication*. Norwood, NJ: Ablex Publishing Corporation, 1984.

Wittgenstein, Ludwig. Trans. Linda L. McAlister and Margarete Schättle. *Remarks on Colour*. Oxford: Blackwell, 1977.

Zumthor, Peter. *Atmospheres: Architectural Environments – Surrounding Objects*. Basel: Birkhäuser, 2005.

2

A DAY IN THE LIFE

Personal Space

The sound of a room. It comes down to this, the space or spaces out of which all this listening must take place. Sound seeks out, flows into, all the crevices and corners of a room in which it is made, or into which it enters from an exterior source. It changes the character of the space for the duration of its audibility, a duration which may be preserved temporally by the scale and shape of the room, or more permanently by recording. It may also be preserved in its essence through memory. Any particular space accommodates sound, welcomes it or repels it, according to its prevailing physical situation and its architectural characteristics. It interacts with the sound on its own terms, mitigated by certain cosmetic or temporary circumstances such as décor, furnishings and/or the presence of people, further depending on how they might be dressed at the time, and how completely they populate the space. We move through sound, while at the same time, sound ebbs and flows around us, sometimes enveloping us, sometimes receding. In order to understand this better, I wish to analyse a single typical day, with the aid of a recorder as witness. Before proceeding further into other rooms in subsequent chapters, it is necessary to explore the subjective world, because *we* are the listening device through which time speaks.

To begin then, at the start of the day; the room in which I write, in which I am writing these words at this moment in time, is a small office, about eight feet by ten feet. The time is just before 6.00 a.m. The silent clock on the wall over the desk reminds me that it is time to start. It is late November and outside it is still dark, but this room only has one window, to the left side and behind me, and the blinds are down. Not that there would be anything to see outside, because the window opens straight onto a wall. Under the window there is a bank of electrical equipment, old technology I keep to record and preserve archive media: a reel-to-reel tape machine, a DAT recorder, a mini-disc player, a CD copier, a turntable for vinyl. The room is also full of media: under all the technology, there are rows of vinyl albums, about 2,000, many of them jazz and classical music. There are also lines of CDs, tapes, cassettes and mini-discs, a lifetime of collecting and making sounds. I think of myself as sitting here in near silence, but just look at all that sound!

The walls are pure white, and on the desk there is a pot of pens, a printer, a radio, and a two-volume set of the *Oxford English Dictionary*. Also a piece of wood sculpture, made for me by my friend, the carver John Fuller, shaped from applewood. It stands about eighteen inches tall, and is a section of a whole trunk of a tree, out of which an androgynous face is in the process of emerging. John carved it for me shortly before he died. It represents a small sound in the act of surfacing out of silence. I find myself dwelling on it every morning as I begin to think about what I will write that day. It seems to symbolise for me the beginning of things, the moment of genesis, the magic stillness of possibility.

Something else; something that, although I am enclosed in this secure space, remains a potential door through which I may be interrupted; the very electronics that enable this room, also provide the ultimate disturbance and distraction. I switch my phone off. On the computer, I deactivate the internet. Even the possibility that the phone might ring, or an email might 'ping' onto the screen, the very idea itself, emits a tiny sound, a disturbance at the back of the mind. The telephone in particular is no respecter of privacy; like an egocentric intruder who bursts into a room and interrupts whatever is going on without warning or consideration, the phone does not discriminate in terms of timing. This is not to say that it is not vital, and welcome and often life-saving. It is just to make the point that when one is listening for the elusive whispers of ideas to emerge, everything else is a distraction, and at this moment, it is important to make a start; the first sound needs to originate from here. There is also on my desk my pocket recorder, which is recording now. The house is quiet. What am I hearing? What am I missing that my recorder will tell me about afterwards? What is the sound of this room? I listen.

This room is a good place to listen and write, built onto the side of the house, and so in a sense outside, separate from the sounds of the building. The main road into the city is behind me, and the first cars are passing as this Monday morning begins. Only sounds. I am aware of the pad-pad of my fingers on the keys of the Mac. I am aware of the moments when I pause, and listen, or just reflect on the next words I will write, this and this and this that you are now reading. I have a sense of talking to you through this silence and the silence from which the words emerge, like the calm face on the Fuller carving beside me, listening. The writer Annie Dillard wrote about her study, the place where she wrote her book *The Writing Life*. I have that book beside me now, and reach for it to remind me of what she said. Like mine, her room was eight by ten feet in its dimensions, actually a prefabricated tool shed. She refers to it as 'a cockpit'. Apart from the audio transfer kit in my room, our spaces feel similar. She has a printer, a photocopier, a computer. Of it, she writes:

> The study affords ample room for one. One who is supposed to be writing books. You can read in the space of a coffin, and you can write in the space of a tool shed meant for mowers and spades.
>
> *(Dillard, 1990, p. 26)*

My space used to be a garage long before we owned the house, before it was plastered and whitewashed and fitted with heating and turned into this tiny room. I love Dillard's assessment of the requirements of her writing room: 'Appealing workplaces are to be avoided. One wants a room with no view, so imagination can meet memory in the dark' (ibid.). I put her book to one side, now I have reminded myself of those words, and reflect. I am writing to you from a small pool of light thrown by a tiny desk light, literally surrounded by darkness. There is also, each time I pause, the darkness – or the whiteness – of silence, punctuated by the occasional brushing sound of a passing car. I have no visual clues as to the nature of the day so far: all my clues are auditory. This room has a flat roof, so I know if it is raining. It is like sheltering in a cave. This morning it is not raining, and it isn't windy, because if it were, I would hear the beech trees at the back of the house roar and creak.

This is as fundamental and ground-zero as I can reach in my quest for the sound of a room, this little personal space. It seems a good place to use as a yard-stick, from which to emerge to interrogate the sounds of other spaces. Unlike the library, there are few sounds I would expect to intrude here; it is a space, as near as anything, that I feel I can control, unless someone comes to the door. It is a place to write, but it is also a place to listen, and to read, and to simply contemplate, without the objects of interference with which we surround ourselves. It is salutary to consider how little we do this: to simply sit and listen. Once I remember someone I was working with suggesting that a radio studio is a 'no place', a blank canvas, an anonymous space awaiting a meaning. I prefer to think of it as a room of infinite possibility, of limitless potential. My office feels like that too; this is also where I come back to listen to the recordings I have made from elsewhere, a neutral environment in which to assess voices and resonances from elsewhere. It is of limited use to listen to the sound of a place *in* the place itself, unless cocooned within the internalising environment of headphones. It is like trying to pay attention to a recorded conversation while conversing with the person to whom you are talking.

I have been writing for nearly an hour now. I know this without looking at the clock, because a gentle 'tick' to my right tells me that the central heating has come on in the house, which it does at this time every morning. Outside the traffic sounds are building, but it is still dark and there are no visuals of day edging through the blinds as yet. Still some way to go before the sky will be light, but there is a sense that time is moving again. Time to stop for a while, have a coffee, and switch off the recorder. I'll listen to what the Tascam remembers of this later.

Rooms on the Road

As human beings we guard our personal space jealously, seeking to preserve an essence of it and move within it as we step out of our door. After all, we have created the sound of the rooms in which we live. I remember the sound of the empty house, as we were moving in, and how we have domesticated its sonic voice with our furnishings. I think what it will sound like again when I am gone, when it is stripped of what Juhani Pallasmaa has called 'the affability of a lived-in home, in which sound is reflected and softened by the numerous surfaces of objects of personal life' (Pallasmaa, p. 54). Every house in this street, in this city, has its own sound, which to its owners says 'home'.

> Every building or space has its characteristic sound of intimacy or monu-
> mentality, invitation or rejection, hospitality or hostility. A space is under-
> stood and appreciated through its echo as much as through its visual shape,
> but the acoustic percept usually remains as an unconscious background
> experience.
>
> *(Ibid.)*

The character of the public world changes, becomes noisier, more invasive, some-times more threatening, and to counter this there are private strategies the indi-vidual has at their disposal to enable the simulation of personal space, the creation of virtual rooms to generate the idea of solitude, even in the most crowded places. The mobile phone here reverses its threat of intrusion; now it becomes our refuge. In socially awkward situations, where we might once have given ourselves something to do by lighting a cigarette, now we busy ourselves by checking emails, or social media, putting physical and invisible screens between ourselves and the world. By plugging in earbuds or a headset, we make the bar-rier more palpable; at one and the same time sending the signal 'do not disturb', while closing the door on sonic intrusion and focusing upon the internal messa-ging and companionship of a favourite radio station, a podcast or our personally selected playlist. Wherever we are, we carry our room. Who can blame us for preserving ourselves in this way?

The 10.47 train, Liverpool Lime Street to London Euston. Smooth, double-glazed pendolino carriages racing through flooded November English fields in warm, air-conditioned comfort, the grey rainstorm outside silent, the interior like an open plan office, full of businesspeople on computers, shielded from the incessant public announcements by their chosen audio programmes, bypassing the cushioned acoustic of the car, and plugging directly into their individual consciousness.

Everyone has their own space, personalising it as soon as they occupy it. Luggage stowed, seats adjusted, and more seats are occupied, and everyone settles again. A man and a woman are talking quietly, discussing a plan for a meeting; when they leave the train at Crewe, I imagine them continuing their conversation in another room, perhaps a taxi, or a different train. These are the momentarily encountered contacts that move on and outwards as our rail room picks up speed again, and there is a sense of being stationary while the landscape moves past at over a hundred miles an hour. Private sound choices on headsets provide situations in which we inhabit one place sonically, while moving through another visually. Listening to a radio feature about ghost stories for half an hour absorbs me totally, while at the same time I am still able to take in the stark image of a solitary oak tree standing alone in the midst of a huge field that the storms have transformed to a lake bounded by hedges. Haunted houses full of spectral rooms of the imagination, peopled by presences in shadows, metaphors for isolation, exclusion, solitude, loneliness, the denial of the right of communication. Not only am I in two places simultaneously, but in two time-worlds. The lateral, temporal progress of the documentary moves on at its own pace, while already, in the time it has taken to write this, the drowning tree is miles behind, unseen until the next train passes, and perhaps another passenger subliminally registers its solitude.

For the rest, there is the smooth hum of the machine, and time to relax. This is a very different travel experience to standing crushed on a stopping commuter train, surrounded by fellow-victims, moved like cattle from one place to another in what feel less like train carriages and more like containers. I am aware that long-distance rail travel – when it is working as it should – is its own experience, all the more so when I reach journey's end, and the electric doors slide open, and the hurtling hubbub of the London terminus breaks forcibly into the cocoon in which I have been protected throughout the trip so far.

Outside, I am met by a friend with a car. We are heading south of the river, to Goldsmiths, The University of London at New Cross. It is a familiar journey, and my friend is an expert at negotiating his way through the traffic of Holborn and across Waterloo Bridge. Nevertheless, conversation is at a minimum for the first part of the journey as he concentrates. With his permission, I record, listen and look as London changes around me. Crossing the bridge, the river opens up a vista of the city, and the car engine slips into higher gear for a while. We do not listen to the radio. There is engine noise, but it is a large, powerful car, and there is a sense of once again being in a calm, civilised room, separated by glass from the unpredictable routine of street life. Mostly, it is the visual that wins over sound in such situations, briefly taking in the text on the National Theatre's scrolling ticker screens, before the streets close in again as we pass Waterloo station and The Old Vic Theatre. Memory is at work here, layers of time, years of experiences as the road weaves out past Elephant and Castle towards Deptford, Greenwich, Blackheath. I sit back and enjoy the ride, secure in the knowledge that I have a sonic witness at work between us in the glove tray, enabling me to relive this journey later.

Playback

When I come to review the sounds of the day, as so often, I am surprised at how much sound information is going on around me, now I have no distractions. Our eyes do not have to see everything; we can close them. Yet as Voegelin reminds me, 'sound constantly enters my ears, bounding around in there, declaring their interest even if I am not listening' (Voegelin, p. 11). Because the ears are open, the brain acts as a mediator, focusing perception on the matter in hand. Just as we have acknowledged the images supplied in our peripheral vision, we may select or otherwise the sound that is relevant to the moment. Subliminally, however, we bank it all in the mind. If we absorbed it all simultaneously, what super-beings we might be, if we could tolerate the multi-media overload experience of complete perception:

> Listening produces a sonic life-world that we inhabit, with or against our will, generating its complex unity. Sound involves me closely in what I see; it pulls the seen towards me as it grasps me by my ears. Sound renders the object dynamic. It makes it "tremble with life" and gives it a sense of process rather than a mute stability… Muteness by contrast numbs the auditory engagement. It applies a local anaesthetic and disables the hearing process.
>
> *(Ibid.)*

This may enable our ability to self-preserve, acting as a screen of protection, or on the other hand it may engender sonic insensitivity bred from the same source; by putting on the headset, we augment our desire to separate ourselves from prevailing sound by placing an alternative to it between us and the surrounding source, a wall of deliberately selected sound to exclude 'found' sound. The sounds of that train journey are not intrusive, yet that very fact draws attention to extraneous sound events, making them, in relative terms, important. Had the sound bed of the train been louder, I would have noticed these occasional events less. I am old enough to have experienced rail travel in the steam age, over unwelded lines. Personal memory, aided by recording, reminds me of sonic comparisons with the past. The defining internal sound of trains used to be the 'clickety-clack' over the joints in rails, punctuated by a cacophonous chatter as the carriages crossed complex points interchanges. The much higher prevailing sound levels forced conversation volumes up in competition, and as the train accelerated from a standing stop, the steam engine made its presence felt like a snorting giant animal, depending on its proximity to where one was seated. This journey has a purring continuity that becomes a sound bed for any signals laid over it. There is the low electronic sound of a door closing, curious unexplained soft 'bleeps' over the intercom, and when the announcements begin, either human or robot, they burst in with a relative volume that startles, presaged by a doorbell-like 'bing-bong'. I hear the approach of stewards, and the kitchen sounds of cups and the pouring of coffee, murmur of voices offering snack options. This awakens the society of the carriage, and suddenly there is more quiet conversation. Listening at various points in the journey, as stations come and go, and some of the occupants are replaced by others, a dialect expert would be interested in the changes in tone colour, accent and perhaps even the nature of the conversation. The recorder interrogates all this with an unprejudiced ear. All this is foreground sound, behind, beyond and underneath, there is simply the hum of the machine, with almost no sense of motion, or the sheer speed at which we are moving down the map. It creates a momentary illusion; perhaps we were not moving at all, my aural sense suggests, perhaps it was the landscape outside that was moving rather than us? The prevailing ambience and the sounds within it conjure the pictures in the mind as if for the first time. Sound also exists temporally, in the passing moment, unlike a photograph which remains fixed where and when it was taken. We travel through a sound recording as we travel through music, or a landscape, place-by-place, note-by-note, instant-by-instant, sound-by-sound, replicating the experience of when it all happened for the first time. The sound of the world is music in this sense, and as we listen again, it is always in the present tense at the split second of hearing.

Next, I turn my attention to the recorded sound of the car journey. The first thing to note is that this is palpably a shared space, so it cannot be a substitute for a room of one's own, as represented by the vehicle so many of us occupy as we travel to and from work, or on shopping trips; in those instances we are entering a familiar domestic space, for which we can claim ownership, manipulating its interior as we would the objects around us in the home. As Bull has said,

> the cultural meaning of the automobile as a privatised entity is inscribed into its very origin. From the move away from travelling collectively in trains at the beginning of the twentieth century, to the discomfort of inhabiting restricted spaces with strangers, to the desire for smooth, unbroken journeys unfettered by timetables.
>
> *(Bull, p. 358)*

The car awaiting us each morning on the drive or in the garage to take us to our own everyday place of work is a metaphor for home, an extension of who we are, and the chosen embodiment of many of our personal traits and characteristics. Little wonder then that our councils and transport operators struggle to persuade us to give up a space that can be described as one of the most intimate rooms we possess, more private even than a room in our own house, because in our car space we can control all intrusions, simply by closing the door and switching off any mobile devices. If we need guidance as to where to go, we may turn on the voice of the GPS navigation system, talking to us in the voice of our choice, and we may select music or speech to entertain us. Everything has the capacity to be personalised and organised according to taste, apart, that is, from the very sound of the engine and road noise outside. Even these, we have the capacity to drown out, simply by turning up the volume on the in-car entertainment system, perhaps even choosing to join in ourselves. The car is anything but a silent space, but the internal sounds it supplies at our command have the potential to register significant subliminal messages, by virtue of the fact that we absorb these audio signals while engaged in other activities, namely negotiating the roads on which we travel. I have noted in my own habits that at times where my concentration on the journey is heightened by complex traffic situations, I have found it necessary to turn the volume of my music down. The morning commute cocooned in our mobile personal room may be the potent source of musical 'ear-worms' for our subsequent day:

> The car is one of the most powerful listening environments today, as one of the few places where you can listen to whatever you like, as loud as you like, without being concerned about disturbing others, and even singing along at the top of your voice – the car is the most ubiquitous concert hall, and the "bathroom" of our time.
>
> *(Stockfeld, quoted by Bull, p. 359)*

On this particular journey across London however there is no in-car entertainment, and while the actual event was peppered with a smattering of social conversation, now, listening back to the recording, my attention is drawn to the sonics of the car, and the language of interaction between machine and the environment through which it travels. As we wait to pull off, there is the sound of seat belts being engaged, the rustle of clothing, the turn of the ignition key and the low purr of the engine. It is raining, and I hear the windscreen wipers come to life. The air-conditioning fan starts, and I remember now that the windows were a little steamy before we drove away. I can follow the journey through a combination of memory of the event itself, and recorded sound clues. The indicator is on, but the car has come to a stop after a few yards. This must be where we were stationary at the traffic lights, before turning onto the Euston Road. Now we accelerate, moving off smoothly. There is the faint noise of traffic outside, but not much; I am taken aback by how well insulated modern cars are, even from their own sound. And yet there is a curious, incessant internal rattle coming from somewhere inside that I cannot identify. I come to the conclusion that it must be the Tascam recorder itself, placed in the well between us, picking up the vehicle's vibrations transmitted up from the road. Would an expert in automobiles be able to discern that we were travelling in a Volkswagen Golf automatic? I suspect some would. By concentrating on the audio and reading the clues, I can just follow the narrative of the journey: this must be Kingsway, approaching the underpass… Now we are out onto Waterloo Bridge… Now the indicator is going again. We must be turning by the Old Vic… and so on. At one point, my friend remembers he needs to pick something up from a shop. The car pulls over, the engine cuts, sound of a seat belt and his driver's door opens and then slams, creating a slight blast of air that impacts on the microphone. Near internal silence, and I realise that at this point, it must have been raining harder than I remember; the only sound comes from the sound of it beating on the windscreen and on the roof.

I relive all this at a distance of time and space, in a neutral studio space where the sound is truly open to examination without confusing the 'here and now' with the 'there and then'. In so doing, it becomes clear that, although we may insulate ourselves from our surroundings within our modern modes of transport, we remain surrounded by events that are symptomatic of a time and place in the world. I also come to understand that, while I can retain the thread of narrative by listening continuously from the start, it only takes a slight lapse in concentration, or a distraction, for me to lose my place in the sonic story. The visitor to this audio journey would probably quickly be lost, only to be put back on track by a few words of narrative exposition, for example: 'Ah, there's the Thames; the Festival Hall's looking inviting this morning' or 'The Old Vic. Is this where we turn?' A car journey is stranger than we may think: an immobile interior, travelling through a landscape.

Back in my own office, I backtrack across the day to review the early morning recording I made within this very room, where it all started in what seems to be an age ago now. Even after focusing closely on relatively calm and ostensibly uneventful soundscapes as the train and the car, this playback process is salutary. Devoid of anything visual, separated from the thought processes that were going on at the time, the recording takes on a new meaning… or rather lack of it. What would this convey to anyone who was given no context for listening? I suspect quite little; there is the presence of the room, and the soft tapping of the computer keys. Very occasionally there is a little traffic noise, but less than I remember it at the time. The whole listening experience is minimalist to the extent of being tedious on one level. 'An unlabelled tape is a blank tape', my first teacher in radio admonished. Once a context is supplied, the brain may do the rest. A good radio drama producer understands that even a tiny clue has the capacity to ignite the imagination. Like looking at the nameless faces from the past in an old family photograph album, we need help to make sense of things, a key to unlock the door of meaning. Once turned, we inhabit the sound room on our terms, free to move around it and 'read' it.

And yet, when attended to with a different set of values, resigned to accept what little sound there is on its own level, to abandon the impatience and desire for action, for something to happen, the need for a dynamic narrative to which human beings are so conditioned, I can hear the playback in a different way. Now the light 'pad-pad' of the soft MacBook keys hypnotises me with the variations of rhythm, and the subtle breathing of the room soothes. Let the meaning dawn in its own time. It is possible to 'read' a storyline of sorts into even this; the moments where the writer pauses to reflect, the moments when he stops to listen, the slight shift of body position as he sits back, then forward again. Is it possible to use the words already written above as a kind of score to follow, while listening to the 'musical soundtrack' of the recording? Or might it be possible to simply pay attention to the sound, ideally on headphones, and use the experience as a kind of meditation? Played without contextual information to a third party, there is very little meaning here in the conventional sense. Nevertheless, there is the existence of a place and time here, even if its sum effect is to send the listener to sleep. Here, the very absence of activity turns the slightest additional minute sound into a 'happening'. Against the bed of stillness, the moments when the typing stops evoke some sort of anticipation; and then there is the 'major' event when I pause and pick up Annie Dillard's book, leaf through the pages as I look for the reference I need, then put it down again and continue writing. It reminds me of some sort of Samuel Beckett-like experience, in which inaction is punctuated by small but detailed moments of activity, made important within the relative scheme of things. There is no plot development in my audio drama, and very little to go on unless you know it was early in the morning on a winter's day in England, and set in the small space of a studio, a kind of 'non-place' in which the only things that happen are mostly of the imagination. Without those directions, it is largely meaningless. It is however, an eloquent example of the (almost) blank canvas upon which the world happens sonically. We are touched by sound, one might say, literally, as it enters us, vibrates through us, as we cover our ears to shut out its excesses, or lean forward to grasp its minutiae, always seeking for something to make a meaning.

I am also reminded, in the moment of writing these words, of *Silence*, a remarkable film by Pat Collins, in which a sound recordist called Eoghan, used to capturing the cacophonous sounds of modern life, travels through remote westerly areas of Ireland in a quest to grasp the essence of silence. In one scene, as he sets up his equipment to record in a field far from human habitation, a man approaches him, and asks him what he is doing? Eoghan tries to explain that he is attempting to record the sound of the natural world without human intervention. The man, having listened to him, pauses and reflects, and then says: 'Ah!… So YOU'RE here!' It is a telling moment in the film; we affect the sound of a place simply by being present in it. Taking this into account, my recording of my own room gains some more context, being as it is the room itself, playing its own music, with interruptions by me. Even if I remain completely still, even if I breathe as lightly as I am able, I am interacting with the space around me, and my presence in relation to the walls and ceiling makes the space in some way acoustically different.

Sitting in a Room

One of the most famous experiments in the dialogue between a human being and room also comes to mind: the American composer Alvin Lucier's remarkable piece *I am sitting in a room*. I have two recordings of this work, which involves

Lucier's voice reading a simple statement, re-recorded and played back into the same room numerous times. The first of these was made in his living room at Middletown, Connecticut in October 1980, while the second was recorded as a DVD by the film-makers Viola Rusche and Hauke Harder at the Crowell Hall of Wesleyan University in 2013. It was a place Lucier knew well, having been a faculty member for many years. During March 1970, he had made his first successful recording of the piece in a rented apartment shortly after joining the university.

The thesis behind the work is very simple. The speaker reads a straightforward, unadorned, functional text: just a few sentences, explaining what he is doing and what his intentions are. In the later recordings, we hear thirty-two repetitions of the text, and with each repetition the syllables are drawn out and resonated by the acoustic of the room until at the end we cannot distinguish where one word ends and another begins; the text is still there, but unintelligible. Over forty minutes, the meaning of human speech has become harmony between a voice and a space. It came from an idea sparked by a chance conversation between Lucier and a colleague at Brandeis University in 1968. The colleague happened to mention to Lucier that he had attended a lecture by Amar Bose (who went on to establish the Bose acoustic wave system and other developments) at the Massachusetts Institute of Technology (MIT), where Bose was a professor. During his talk, Bose had demonstrated a technique for testing loudspeakers by recycling sounds. Little else was discussed by the two men during this corridor conversation, but something was triggered in Lucier's mind about the possibilities of recycling sound. His first attempt, in a basic institutional teaching room at the university, was unsatisfactory, so he decided to set up a more controlled experiment in his rented apartment. For this, Lucier borrowed two Nagra tape recorders, and positioned them outside his living room, so the machines would not contribute any extraneous sound to the process. Inside, he set up a Beyer microphone and a KLH loudspeaker. Without too much thought, he then scribbled his text, the words that were to be the subject of this metamorphosis; just a simple description of what he was doing. He deliberately avoided any elevated or aesthetic content, confining himself to a short paragraph that was completely utilitarian.

Before proceeding, it was necessary to take account of his immediate sonic surroundings. Outside the apartment, there was a bar that closed at 11.00 pm, so he waited until all was quiet externally; fortunately for his purposes, it was a snowy night, so few cars were on the road. Inside, he switched off the apartment's refrigerator and radiators to ensure, as much as possible, domestic quiet. Lucier then started tape machine one, entered the room, and recorded his text. Having done so, and stopped the tape, he rewound it, ready for playback, and placed the loudspeaker on the chair where he had been sitting. Next, he set the second machine to record, and played back the first recording, committing this too to tape. In that first attempt, he repeated the process sixteen times. Later versions were increased to thirty-two repetitions, but for Lucier's purposes, by the sixteenth repeat, he had proved the point to himself sufficiently to know that he had, through the interacting of a simple text with a room, created a joint 'composition', a collaboration with the space itself. Through the time span of a sleepless night, the parts of his speech that excited resonant frequencies became stronger, and those that did not were eliminated, so that by the end of sixteen generations, only the resonant frequencies of the room, excited by speech, are audible. It is a hypnotic and eerie listening experience. Most significant is the gradual shift from intelligibility to unintelligibility, including a perceptible moment at a certain point where the work ceases to be words, and turns itself to music, moving from the cognitive to the pure senses, and then progressing onwards until the room itself seems to be singing its haunting song. This experiment in essence sums up the performative role of an environment to which I shall return later.

Lucier's work received a reference in a radio drama adaptation of Nigel Kneale's cult TV supernatural thriller *The Stone Tape* in 2015 on BBC Radio, a play about scientists experimenting with new sound technology working in an apparently haunted house. The reimagined version was written by Matthew Graham and Peter Strickland, who also directed it for *Somethin' Else* productions. In a climactic scene, they are trying to simulate the tonal and acoustic qualities of a cellar in which they have witnessed the sound of a disembodied scream, by recording a human scream and rerecording it. It is precisely the same principle, and eloquently supports the play's imaginary premise, that walls may seem to have voices that events have stored within the fabric of a building. While this was never Lucier's intention in creating *I am sitting in a room*, the piece does undeniably possess a strange otherworldly quality that moves the listener from the prosaic to the elliptical.

Voices from Next Door

As Lucier identified in his set-up, extraneous sound in such an experiment was a distraction. In many situations, however, our rooms do not exist in sonic isolation. No space – or at least most spaces – can be described as a complete auditory island. Within the domestic environment, found sound can catch us unawares through the nature of its transmission. We carry expectations of the familiar, so we notice when acoustic circumstances alter it. Birdsong belongs to the great outdoors; it is a sound we step *into* when we move beyond the confines of our interiors. To hear the sound *inside* a building alters perception, not only because it does not belong there, but because it is changed by the acoustic it now inhabits. I have heard a pigeon making its mourning sound on my chimney, and it demands attention I would not give it if I heard it in the context of the garden. Dillard observed the same phenomenon with a mockingbird that habitually nested around her home, striking up its song in high places, one of which being her chimney: 'When he sings there, the whole chimney acts as a sound box, like the careful emptiness inside a cello or violin, and the notes of the song gather fullness and reverberate through the house' (Dillard, 1998, p. 106). The sudden spontaneous unfamiliarity of a known sound can make it new and strange and lodge its refreshed identity in the imagination and memory forever. Beyond these physical walls are other rooms, some of which possess no partitions or ceilings, and are full of weather and a 'found' music of their own. They beat on our windows and doors and roofs, declaring themselves, adding their presence to the sounds within. Into the relative stillness of the office comes a gentle 'pad-pad' of something overhead; my neighbour's cat is on his morning patrol over my head.

The world brushes against us. We may shut it out, but its voices are still murmuring, speaking, singing and shouting on the other side of the wall, beyond the windows, against the glass. Discussing this with a British-Canadian sound recordist friend Rob Bridgett, the idea of the intrusion of weather became a topic. Rob lives in Quebec, but he was reminded of some domestic recordings he made during the winters of 2013–15, when he was living on Patrick Street, St John's, Newfoundland. It is terrain we both know well. I have spent some time in Newfoundland, studying the oral culture and making some documentary programmes that have been broadcast both on BBC and CBC Radio. As Rob explains, the sound evokes the place through memory:

> Our house on Patrick Street was just a few doors up the road from one of the oldest radio stations in North America, VOWR run out of the Wesley United Church – they'd play very odd selections of 1950's and 60's easy listening interspersed with funeral announcements.[1]

Immediately I remember listening while staying in St John's and working for a time at Memorial University just out of town. I visited the station, so I know the road well; VOWR is indeed a venerable organisation. Staffed by volunteers, it first signed on 24 July 1924 under the call sign **8WMC**, which stood for the **W**esley **M**ethodist **C**hurch. Reverend Joseph G. Joyce (1889–1959) started the station to provide church services for people unable to attend events, due to ill health or other circumstances. From these beginnings it soon expanded to provide public service announcements and entertainment, today sponsored by the sale of commercial advertising.

The island of Newfoundland, once a British protectorate but today an outpost of Canada on the east coast, facing into the Atlantic, is a place where the weather is a factor in everything. Two of Rob's recordings in particular captured this sense. One of these was a heavy rain storm, the other a night when the wind reached high gale force and the empty room in which he had situated his recorder resonated like a drum.

> For the rain and the wind storms both were quite extreme weather events where I was compelled (excitedly) to record. In the case of the room – I knew the wind storm would peak, and as it was quite late at night and I wanted to sleep, I decided to just leave the recorder alone in the spare room at the back of the house (facing the bay it gets the brunt of the wind)

> allowing me to sleep without ruining the recording! Incidentally, I have slept in that back room during a bad windstorm and it was like being on a boat or a turbulent aircraft as the wooden house shakes and moves during the storm in a way that really isn't conducive to a good night's kip. I probably expected the recording to be more 'creaky and storm like' – but that's all from my experience of the room moving and obviously doesn't come across in the sound alone.
>
> *(Ibid.)*

To an objective, dispassionate listener, the recordings are eloquent. Unfamiliar with the actual physical space, I am offered a picture for my imagination to furnish of a room that clearly is on a frontier of sound. This is a study in dynamics, of rising and falling crescendos, affording at times a palpable sense of danger, a feeling that the elements might at certain points threaten to overwhelm the house itself. In contrast, there is a heightened feeling of the stillness in the empty room. It is eerie, this sound of an empty room 'listening' to weather on its own. Unlike the sound clues provided by the car acoustics described earlier, there is no personal memory for me here to relive an experience. There is only a feeling of pure sensation, in which the 'found' music of the elements plays on the external surfaces of the room making a shape of it, even suggesting to the 'blind' senses colours, and objects – chairs, a bed, pictures – all of which originate not from the physical reality of the place, which is unknown to me, but from a composite sonic set of suggestions taking me to a mysterious shadowy recollection from my own past. Like me, Rob records such events in an attempt at preserving an essence to be revisited in future time, in another place:

> I think a lot of these recordings are for my personal reference, so I can relive those moments and experience them again… The act of recording definitely goes beyond just capturing a texture for use as background tone or ambience in post production sound contexts. There's an emotional connection to the sounds and the places – and to some extent the time travel that becomes possible in the re-listening of those recordings.
>
> *(Ibid.)*

Memory is a bank of sound that plays silently in recollection. We measure new experience through our history of experience, and the contrasts of the time through which we pass create metaphorical rooms we revisit like movements in a symphony or a string quartet. Sound does not need to assault us in order to convey its continuing presence in the mind. There could be few greater contrasts in the study of auditory perception than between a storm-beaten bedroom in Newfoundland and the murmuring ambience of the Members' Room at Lord's Cricket Ground in North London. Yet for Tony Stoller, a media historian and MCC member, it is a potent place, a room full not only of the subtle sounds of the present, but of suggestion, implication and history. Outside the ground, at the junction of Wellington Road and St John's Wood Road, there is a bas relief which prepares the visitor for the hallowed tradition within, by quoting the final line of Henry Newbolt's famous poem which begins with the words, 'a breathless hush in the close tonight'. In the Long Room of the Lord's Pavilion itself, Stoller hears a mixture of *sotto voce* conversation, murmurs of appreciation or otherwise for the game itself, the occasional burst of applause, and even the odd snore or two:

> The sound seems to seep into the walls of the room, mingling with pictures of Edwardian and Victorian cricket, the portrait of WG Grace, the cricket ball bowled by Jahangir Khan to Tom Pearce on the ground in 1936, which struck and killed a swallow in flight, and the curved bats of the Hambledon Men of the late eighteenth century. You can sit there and hear all around you the end of Empire, and the long withdrawing hum of the centuries. There is, literally, nothing like it in the world.[2]

The music that plays in an internal space is ongoing, sometimes illusive, but sometimes strongly eloquent, reminding us that it is sound that haunts space, with or without us. I return to one of the opening statements of this chapter, in which I wrote:

> sound seeks out, flows into, all the crevices and corners of a room in which it is made, or into which it enters from an exterior source. It changes the character of the space for the duration of its audibility…

The storm, with its rain and wind, claims a part of the ownership of our privacy. At this point, I must step out from the objective security of the observer, safe within a secure space, and encounter these rooms waiting outside, striving to gain admittance, full as they may be of wind, rain, and all that turning a corner or crossing a road may bring to change my own personal internal space, and break into memory, the place inside the mind that has to interpret all this. Insulation from what lies outside the door is so often an illusion: 'There was a man dwelt by a churchyard', wrote M.R. James, in an eponymous story taking its title from the child Mamilius in Shakespeare's *A Winter's Tale*:

> His house had a lower story of stone and an upper story of timber. The front windows looked out on the street and the back ones on the churchyard… that night, as he lay in his bed upstairs, a moaning wind began to play about the house, and he could not go to sleep.
>
> *(James, pp. 605/608)*

Not all the rooms in the world are manmade, but that does not mean they do not shape us with their sound.

Notes

1 Rob Bridgett, personal communication with the author.
2 Tony Stoller, interview with the author. Reproduced with permission.

References

Bull, Michael. 'Soundscapes of the Car: A Critical Study of Automobile Habitation', in Michael Bull and Les Back, *The Auditory Culture Reader*. Oxford: Berg, 2003, pp. 357–74.
Dillard, Annie. *The Writing Life*. New York: Harper Collins, 1990.
Dillard, Annie. *Pilgrim at Tinker Creek*. Norwich: Canterbury Press, 1998.
James, M.R. *Collected Ghost Stories*. Ware: Wordsworth Editions, 1992.
Pallasmaa, Juhani. *The Eyes of the Skin: Architecture and the Senses*. Chichester: Wiley, 2012.
Voegelin, Salomé. *Listening to Noise and Silence*. New York: Continuum, 2010.

3

PERFORMING ROOMS

Show Time

A room in the traditional, physical sense is a contained landscape, a box in which air is surrounded by walls, a ceiling and floor, affected by contents, furnishings, decorations, size and physical shape. It is thus a sound world in which the transmissions have finite boundaries, and governed by the individual properties of the environment. Maekawa, Rindel and Lord identify two major characteristics of indoor sound fields that differentiate them from uninterrupted terrain.

> (1) The sound intensity at a receiving point remote from the source is not attenuated as much as in free space even if the distance is large. (2) Reverberation occurs due to the reflected sound arriving after the source has stopped.
>
> *(Maekawa, Rindel and Lord, p. 56)*

The key word in these two points is 'source', the implication being that in order for a space to release its sonic character, it has to be 'ignited' so to speak, a spark of sound 'struck', to reveal itself acoustically. Of course, it is possible to gain a sense of an apparently totally silent place simply by listening. There are properties contained in minute movements of air within an internal space, just as there are in a landscape where the horizon is many miles away. Our first instinct, particularly as performers, is to engage in a sonic dialogue with a room, even if it is with no more than a clap of the hands. Babies and very young children do it instinctively, sometimes to the embarrassment of those around them. A space is where we find ourselves at any one time, and if we are to work in or with it, or live in it, we must know how its audio presence affects us. We design our rooms according to our requirements. In theatres, shape, size and form relate crucially to function, depending not only on the type of play or drama, but on the style of production and direction. Multi-functional auditoria become increasingly complex and reactive as technology allows their size and shape to be varied at the press of a button. The very use of words such as 'audience' and 'auditorium' through the study and practice of the performing arts tells us of the significance of sound. It is not the purpose of this book to explore the science of acoustics; there are many works that supply that requirement more than adequately. What draws the attention here is the human relationship to sonic environments, be it through music, the spoken word or aural spectacle. This last is important because, although while an auditorium by virtue of its name underlines the importance of sound, it is also a place of visual witness. To attend a live concert is to *participate* in an experience, rather than to simply *hear* it. When it became technically possible to commit a performance to cylinder and later disc, tape or memory card, from early times, the word 'recording' came into play, implying that this was a *record* of an event, just as verbatim minutes of a meeting are intended to provide as faithful an account as possible of what occurred. Yet even the best and most sophisticated sound system is not capable of replicating, for example, the sheer theatrical visual impact of, say, a staged performance of Gustav Mahler's colossal Eighth Symphony, the 'Symphony of a Thousand', or an evening of grand opera.

As a child of eight or nine, I attended my first symphony concert at Sheffield City Hall, although I cannot remember what I heard, so overwhelmed was I by the onslaught on my senses of the room itself. It was a performance by The Hallé Orchestra, conducted by Sir John Barbirolli, but as I entered the hall, the only sound was a rustling stillness, and a sense of anticipation. I felt as though I was almost the only person in the room. The stage was awaiting its musicians, a few people were filtering in through various doors, and the sheer size of the space, a receptacle for people and sound slowly filling, took my breath away. Between rehearsal and performance, a concert hall or theatre holds its peace, and seems to prepare. To be *there*, sharing the air with the performers and fellow audience members, cannot be fully replicated. There is a rhythmic ritual to an orchestral concert: the gradual increase in audience noise as the hall fills, the single note of the oboe, tuning of the orchestra, followed by applause to greet the arrival of the leader, then the stillness of expectation, and more applause as the conductor comes to the platform, and the room settles in anticipation. Through this gradual sharpening of attention, sound ebbs and flows, and we become increasingly focused upon what is to come; our participatory presence in the moment cannot be replicated. All else, however sophisticated, is eavesdropping, or archiving a memory. In the end, it is a straight comparison between communal sharing against a frozen replaying, fixed and unchangeable, as opposed to the vicissitudes and uniqueness of a moment in time in which what happens next is constantly forming before our senses. For some performers, like The Beatles and Glenn Gould, it became necessary to move from the hall to the studio in order to maintain absolute control over their work. (In the case of The Beatles, audience reaction became so extreme that they could not hear the sound of their own music.) In contrast, others, such as the great conductor Sergiu Celibidache, eschewed the recording studio almost completely, claiming that the live performance in the hall before an audience produced a chemistry that could not be replicated in what he considered to be a sterile technical environment. The recordings we have of his work, notably with the Munich Philharmonic Orchestra of the Bruckner Symphonies, are taken from live radio and TV broadcasts. In this sense, they are third hand, but for those of us who never sat in a hall and heard the original, they are better than nothing. There are recordings of live events that we may treasure, be it Aretha Franklin at a gospel concert, The Who live at Leeds University in 1970, or Jacqueline Du Pré performing the Elgar Cello Concerto, but in the final analysis, if we are honest, such listening only provokes some sort of regret that we were not there when these things happened that first and only time. It is good, but it is *different*, just as listening to a good commentator at a football, baseball or cricket match, conveying the scene and the excitement with all the professionalism at their disposal, is different. To be in the audience, or in the crowd, would surely be the first choice, but we must be content with this. From a performer's perspective, or a participant in a sporting activity, the sense of presence provided by an audience or a crowd can be an active part of the experience and the end result. A great sporting event played out in an empty stadium is hollow. Even rehearsal spaces in which actors and musicians prepare for performance are important in giving a sense of organic development and life. Older buildings with creaks and other sounds of their own have the potential to free a creative artist, as opposed to sound-proofed, hermetically sealed spaces. It may be as though one is feeding off the existing life of a place, as though some rooms may breathe more than others, in tune with ourselves.

Tuning the Room

The very nature of sound is that it is both universal and personal at the same time; we hear a familiar tune, or artist in performance within the context of our memory of the sound of the song, or their voice as it first became familiar to us. This may be as a radio broadcast, a recording or a TV or film presentation. We tend to judge the communal experience using our individual criteria. This raises the question, what is the perfect performance space, and how do we create something that has to be perfect for everyone who inhabits it, performers and audience alike? Internal music performance spaces for generations tended, until the twentieth century to adopt what became known as a 'shoe box' shape, effectively an oblong, with the performers situated at one end, such as the Grosser Musikvereinssaal in Vienna, famous as the opulent location for the Vienna Philharmonic Orchestra's New Year's Day concerts. Jaffe offers us a concise historical perspective:

> From Athens' Greco-Roman Theatre of Athena, built sometime around 424
> B.C., to European palace ballrooms and the first public music halls of the

eighteenth and nineteenth centuries, all indoor performance rooms were narrow in width. To increase the capacity of these narrow rooms, the obvious solution was to extend the length. Following this method, concertgoers from the sixteenth century through the nineteenth would listen to a performance seated at one end of a rectangular room with the orchestra at the other end. Other methods for increasing capacity included shallow balconies and parterres (raised areas surrounding the orchestra floor seating).

(Jaffe, p. 11)

In the work of Marcus Vitruvius Pollio, a Roman architect and engineer who flourished in the first century BC, we have the author of the oldest and most influential work on architecture in existence. For hundreds of years, the specific instructions he provided in his *Ten Books on Architecture* were faithfully followed, and there are many major buildings around the world that demonstrate the influence of his precepts. Sound was among his major preoccupations, and indeed, in Book Five of his writings, he shows us that a theatre auditorium could be a place of radical sonic techniques that made it far from a passive empty space:

> Let bronze vessels be made, proportionate to the size of the theatre, and let them be so fashioned that, when touched, they may produce with one another the notes of the fourth, the fifth, and so on up to the double octave. Then, having constructed niches in between the seats of the theatre, let the vessels be arranged in them, in accordance with musical laws, in such a way that they nowhere touch the wall, but have a clear space all round them and room over their tops.
>
> *(Vitruvius, p. 143)*

It would seem that Vitruvius had a conception of an auditorium as a place of pure sonic sensation, a musical force in its own right, something that was itself a kind of giant wind instrument. He is meticulous in his instructions, to the extent that we may sense his thinking, that a theatre or indeed any performance space is something not only to be constructed, but to be tuned. Yet a little further on, we see that all this has an intensely practical purpose; Vitruvius is installing a sound system:

> On this principle of arrangement, the voice, uttered from the stage as from a centre, and spreading and striking against the cavities of the different vessels, as it comes in contact with them, will be increased in clearness of sound, and will wake an harmonious note in unison with itself.
>
> *(Ibid.)*

What we may regard as pure ornamentation in ancient buildings might well in many cases, have also been designed with practical considerations of acoustics in mind. Through experiments using choirs and recording equipment placed in strategic parts of San Marco in Venice, Howard and Moretti demonstrated that when the architect and sculptor Sansovino made alterations to the interior of the church in the sixteenth century, among the most significant interventions was the transformation of the choir from a mediaeval to a renaissance interior. Working partly in consultation with the composer Adrian Willaert, 'his [Sansovino's] alterations to the chancel…, initiated in the time of Doge Gritti, responded – at least to some degree – to the needs of musical performance' (Howard and Moretti, p. 202). I will return to the matter of sounds in sacred spaces in the next chapter.

The challenges of communicating sound and image across large theatrical spaces are as old as the medium itself. In a cast list, we speak of *Dramatis Personae*, as Stocker reminds, us, and the term 'personae' takes us to the amphitheatres of ancient Greece:

> The "Personae" were the masks used to project the character and voices of the actors into the audience,… most of whom were too far from the stage to see the subtlety of the actor's facial expressions, so the personae were used to visually emphasise the dominant emotional characteristics of the role in an exaggerated form. Because the masks would otherwise cover the mouths of the actor, they were crafted to resonate and thus amplify the human voice. The mouth was always wide open or included a voice projection horn, allowing the actor to focus their voice through the mask while wearing it, animating the character with sound.
>
> *(Stocker, p. 37)*

Creating purpose-built spaces for performance of any kind is highly complex:

> Public halls, like civic auditoria and most commercial rental halls, are for multi-purpose use, so that the reverberation time has to be adequate for both music and speech, but priority must be given to the requirements of the most frequent performance, although unfortunately, it is not easy to anticipate the true requirements.
>
> *(Maekawa, Rindel and Lord, p. 247)*

Sometimes the best-laid plans of the consultant acoustician may be undermined by the desires or requirements of the architect. A certain type of wall-covering, or the placement of a sounding board, may interfere with the overall design and 'look' of an interior, perhaps at the expense of the auditory requirements of the hall. Moreover we may become familiar with, for example, a certain type of orchestral sound largely through older halls, which may indeed have governed artistic decisions and techniques employed by composers such as Haydn, Beethoven and Schubert, when 'the entire musical process – from the composition of a symphonic score to its performance – was based on spaces with similar aural environments' (Jaffe, p. 14). Thus a link between creation and reception existed that generated a particular expectation of what a definitive performance should actually sound like.

The walls, floors, and ceilings of these spaces reflected sound waves in patterns that laid the foundations for the 'traditional" sound of orchestral music, a sound that shaped the qualitative judgements of most performers and audience members to this day.

(Ibid.)

Thus the awarding of a commission to create any new concert hall or performance space may be seen by some as potentially a poisoned chalice, as witness the failure of New York's Philharmonic Hall, in the Lincoln Centre, opened in 1962. The hall was built to a modified 'shoe box' design, with overhead sound reflectors similar to those that had been used with success elsewhere, notably at the Tanglewood Music Pavilion. From the start, the hall was beset with problems; expectations, fuelled by a considerable public relations campaign, were great, and while there were real practical sound issues from the start, as Jaffe says, public opinion was partly shaped by a long and illustrious musical tradition in the city:

> Orchestra players complained that they could not hear themselves, and music critics commented that the hall was too bright and the bass response weak. Their dissatisfaction was compounded by the fact that the New York Philharmonic had moved to the new hall at Lincoln Centre from the much-beloved Carnegie Hall, a hall with a warm, intimate sound that had been burned into the collective memory of the New York musical community for over sixty years. Musical memory (more properly, perhaps, *sonic* memory) plays an important part in the way individuals perceive an aural experience and their subsequent qualitative judgements.
>
> *(Ibid., p. 25)*

Lessons – albeit expensive ones – may be learned from such disasters. After a number of unsuccessful modifications to New York's Philharmonic Hall, the space was replaced in 1976 by the Avery Fisher Hall. Great strides were made in room acoustics, and surrounding publicity opened the public's ears to the fact that 'there was much more to listening to classical music than the tunes' (ibid., p. 26). Since that time, computer simulation and acoustic-model study have enabled far better ideas of what a completed project might sound like, and 'while the exact prediction of room acoustics is still not easy, the creation of acoustic quality is gradually becoming achievable through a scientific approach to the art of musical performance' (Maekawa, Rindel and Lord, p. 246).

Spaces are Doing It for Themselves

Thus far, this chapter has concerned itself with performance spaces designed as receptacles for created human experience. Yet these rooms may be performers in their own right. John Cage's famous 'silent' work, *4' 33"* forced his audience to listen to the room they shared with the performer. It was a crucial moment in the understanding of human and non-human performance. In Cage's own words,

> I listen to it constantly in my life experience. No day goes by without my making use of that piece in my life and work. I listen to it every day…I don't sit down to do it; I turn my attention toward it. I realise that it's going on continuously.
>
> *(Cage, in Gann, p. 186)*

A made space is the expression of an idea that was originally conceived by a human mind and hand. The fact that from the moment of its creation it exists in its own right, does not mean that we do not seek to enhance it and 'improve' it, (sometimes to the detriment of the sonic life of the space itself, as we have seen). This may have been to shape our own sound, or in some cases, to 'tune' the space itself like a musical instrument in its own right. The German Jesuit scholar and polymath Athanasius Kircher (1602–80) might be said to have been the last true Renaissance man, and amongst his fascinations was the idea of the transmission of sound, and what today we might call audio surveillance systems. In particular, he developed a major interest in the concept of the propagation of sound between discreet spaces through a tube. This obsession grew from a specific event in 1638, when he visited Sicily, where, among quarries that had been formerly used as prisons near Syracuse, he was shown a cave with the local name of 'The Ear of Dionysus', where the tyrant Dionysus was said to eavesdrop on his prisoners' conversations. When he was furnished, at his request, with plans and dimensions of the cave, Kircher came to the conclusion that for maximum acoustical effect, the space had been designed to replicate the shape of the human ear. In his book, *Musurgia Universalis*, he makes connections between shapes and sound:

> One may well wonder why the multiplication of sound is so strong in a cone twisted in a spiral. I have certainly pondered long over this matter, finding at last that a helical cone, twisted in a certain ratio, makes some kind of parabola which brings about infinite conglomerations of sound. So it is no wonder that it achieves such energy in the multiplication of sound.
>
> *(Kircher, p. 303, quoted in Godwin, p. 165)*

He also noted the presence of what we have come to know as 'whispering galleries' in which a quiet murmur at one point propagates in circles, reflecting off the walls at every point, until the reflections converge on a listener situated as a distant point. As examples he cites the round tower of Heidelberg Castle, a hall in the Palazzo del Tè in Mantua and no less than the dome of St Peter's in Rome, all well in advance of the well-known English example of St Paul's Cathedral, construction of which did not start until 1675, just five years before Kircher's death. While some of his theories proved to be based on fallacies, the underlying principle behind much of his work, that walls might indeed have ears and voices, was based on the real concerns of the rich and powerful of his time, that welcomed the idea that audio 'snooping' might prove useful and even crucial in the maintenance of power. Today's world might well be overrun with surveillance cameras, but in the seventeenth century, Kircher saw the future of spy and intelligence technology in sound, and in particular with sonic interconnection between spaces within a building. The principle behind the intercom or internal telephone was at the heart of much of this thinking.

The nature of recording within a public arena brings into focus the role of the space itself, in shaping the sound. Thomas Tallis's forty-part motet *Spem in Alium* requires at least the electronic simulation of a cathedral space to give it its true character. The personality of a 'live' performance space in shaping an audience response to music, as opposed a studio acoustic, however sophisticated, may contain nuances that happen through a blend of in-built characteristics, and sometimes, even fortuitous sonic accidents. Eric F. Clarke highlighted this by selecting two recordings of Berlioz's *Symphonie Fantastique*, focusing his attention on the movement entitled 'Scène aux champs'. The symphony is programmatic, and this particular movement 'is conceived as taking place outdoors in a rural setting: Berlioz's programme for this movement starts thus: "Finding himself one evening in the country, he hears in the distance two shepherds piping a *ranz des vache* in dialogue"' (Clarke, p. 96). Clarke contrasts two recordings of this particular section, enacted by a cor anglais and an oboe within the orchestra. One recording was made in 1974, by Colin Davis with the Concertgebouw Orchestra of Amsterdam in the Concertgebouw Hall, while the other, with the London Classical Players conducted by Roger Norrington, was made in 1988 at No. 1 studio, Abbey Road, London. In this comparison, the location becomes crucial in terms of fulfilling listener expectation, given an informed knowledge of Berlioz's intentions and his sonic *mise en scène*.

> Davis's recording [in Concertgebouw Hall] sounds more "picturesque" and evocative of a context that contains real distances (from hill to hill, or field to field) than does Norrington's – though of course the acoustic of the virtual space is completely wrong for a truly outdoor scene. The long reverberation time of the Concertgebouw successfully conveys large spatial volume, but if this cor anglais and oboe were really out in the fields there would be little or no reverberation time at all – a contradiction that listeners seem happy to accept. Arguably then, Davis's recording adopts a more realist approach to the work's programme, coming closer to creating a sounding space that conveys the drama of physical distance; while Norrington's… is much closer to an attempt to capture an historical concert performance – located though it is, ironically, in the Abbey Road studio.
>
> *(Ibid., p. 97)*

Yet the recording studio, with its multiple sound possibilities and its transformative potential, is surely the most versatile of all spaces, a room in which sound can almost literally be 'made'. The Beatles' last album before they turned their backs on live performance and shifted to the studio as an instrument was *Rubber Soul* and the first after that event was *Sgt Pepper's Lonely Hearts Club Band*. They gave up touring in the same year that Glenn Gould gave up 'live' performance: 1966. It signalled a key shift in the role of recording in relation to place. A record was no longer merely a souvenir of a performance: it WAS the performance, definitive, perfect, and at the time, beyond the capabilities of either performers or technical staff to reproduce on stage. The move had been coming for some time, as producers became the real artists in some situations, manipulating the sound of the room to the extent that they were actually working the performers as participating instruments. Key to this development was the work of Brian Wilson of the Beach Boys, and Phil Spector, who in the early to mid-1960s, perfected his 'Wall of Sound' that became more recognisable than the artists themselves. The Spector sound defined itself most in his work with The Ronettes. As Brian Eno said, 'the biggest trend of all was certainly towards this fascination with things that just had their own sound picture… "Be My Baby," where you had this enormous, huge sonic picture with the thinnest voice you've ever heard' (Eno, quoted by Toop, pp. 106–7). Indeed, the fragility of Ronnie Spector's lead vocal, pitched against a sound that generated a gigantic, almost enveloping, ambience, was a key part in the making of the drama. It triggered a shift, in which the nature of commercial popular song production changed, and began its journey to the sometimes completely formative force it is in modern mass market music. From this point, the sound room becomes nothing to do with faithful reproduction of a 'live' performance; the studio is now a magic box, a place the function of which is the creation of illusions. 'Performance', wrote David Toop, looking back on the moment from 1995, 'can never be the same again'.

> One of the first live bands I saw was The Ronettes, supporting The Rolling Stones on their second national tour. On a Ronettes record, teenage life crises were amplified to the scale of major meteorological disturbance. Live, encased in iridescent sheath dresses, stripped of Spector's awesome production, The Ronettes (and the life crises) were reduced to human proportions.
> *(Toop, p. 108)*

As a teenager, I was at another date on that very same tour; I couldn't hear The Rolling Stones because of the audience's reaction, but I heard enough of The Ronettes' performance to know that things had reversed: the performance had become a pale souvenir of the record. As time passed, technology caught up, so that today, when we go to a 'live' pop or rock concert, the greatest compliment we can pay the experience is to say to one another, 'it sounds just like the record'. The stage act now has the capacity to replicate the room in which it was first created, the place where the sonic benchmark was set to which public performance must aspire. Take a song such as 'Believe' by Cher, made in 1998, which demonstrated such a degree of studio manipulation that it created another shift in the relationship between producer, performer and audience, and generated wide-ranging influence on pop copyists seeking to emulate the effects manufactured by the producers Mark Taylor and Brian Rawling.

> Technology has transformed us into giants, bionic superhumans, stateless satellites, omnipresent speakers-in-tongues. We become bigger than we are, louder, displaced or multiplied, or we shrink, intimidated by the waterfall of information. We use technology to protect and isolate ourselves, articulating desires that have been suppressed by technology, trying to replace alienation with techno-spirituality, using contradictory messages to express confusions for which our history has not prepared us.
>
> *(Ibid.)*

In popular culture, the commercial recording studio and the technology with which we fill it makes all things sonically possible, as living up to them in the real world grows increasingly *impossible.*

With or without us, rooms possess the capacity to perform in their own right. Whether or not we hear them, is not a room's concern. A room is built, I furnish it, populate it with objects, and decorate it. Within its parameters, the space is set going like a clock. What happens during its time is a subject for a later chapter, but once it exists, it is both a passive receptacle and an active generator of sound. In December 2019, the sound artist Frazer Merrick created a short impressionistic feature for BBC Radio 3's *Between the Ears* strand, under the title *Hidden Sounds of Coastal Arcades,* based on Walton Pier in north Essex. Britain's coastline, in particular its seaside resorts, is characterised at various points by piers, many of them constructed in Victorian and Edwardian times, the expression of a curious desire for human beings to walk on water, to civilise an elemental space. Merrick's piece, employing binaural sound recordings, used Walton Pier as an example of this architectural form, creating a sometimes surreal and ghostly sound picture of just one such shrine to the act of play, in a work that ran for nine minutes, and was made up of three distinct movements. It begins in the bustling entertainment arcade, full of gaming machines, eloquently including even the strange close 'fizzing' sounds of the electromagnetic fields produced by the machines: thus at several points the audience finds itself actually *listening* to light. From the arcade, the composition – for that is what this is – moves into the fairground outside, and finally the sounds of the water into which the pier intrudes, and upon which it stands.

In selecting this particular pier as his subject, Merrick was focusing on an archetype:

> I myself don't have nostalgic memories of Walton, but I do other seaside towns. Walton is the sort of seaside town you escape to; the wide-open expanses of its huge beaches juxtapose with a more claustrophobic

day-to-day reality for most visitors. It's a place that facilitates and promotes play, and play is a string with which we tie our memories and our friendships together. Walton Pier is a home to this act.

In capturing this, Frazer Merrick utilised sound equipment rather as a screen director might use cameras, employing a variety of microphones to collect a full spectrum of sounds, from the tiny mechanical sounds to widescreen ambiences, from hydrophones in the water, to electromagnetic microphones on the machines to hear the sounds of the circuits controlling the cacophonous and intense atmosphere of music and lights. He also made binaural recordings on the boardwalk, capturing snippets of conversations as families walked past, giving us a brief insight into the sensory experience of being on the pier. Field recording in this context is about collecting a palette of colours the artist can work with in the studio. What evolves out of this process is a sound poem – or rather picture – that moves in and out of realism, by turns naturalistic and surreal, even ghostly and unsettling. Piers are strange places, the product of a wish to civilise the elemental, and arcades, when placed on piers, become part of this illusion.

> Arcades are environments where you lose track of time, and I wanted my piece to do the same. The piece is structured to reflect an actual journey through Walton Pier. Entering through the front doors into the bustling arcade, then into the cacophonous fairground with its waltzers and clattering dodgems, before finishing in peace at the end of the pier – looking out into the expanse of the North Sea. I'm trying to reflect what might be a two or three hour visit in 10 minutes, so by using realism as a compositional technique it allows me to reflect that passing of time, moving between real-time recordings to surreal and abstract compositions. I was inspired by Charles Parker's *Radio Ballads* as well as Steve Reich's *Different Trains*, both compositions which use field recordings in a very musical way.[1]

The work is extremely pictorial, and the overriding imaginative effect is of a small pool of light and sound surrounded by space. Vox pops root it in human memory, but the main voices are non-human, sounds that link generations and punctuate the continuing presence of sea wash. One speaker remembers the geography of the pier through pure sound, noting that he could always tell where he was as he walked along it, by the sonic signals of the various activities. In less than ten minutes, the listener builds a relationship with Walton Pier as it becomes familiar, a friendly place that creates memories and holds affection for those who have known it all their lives.

> Initially I wanted to visit just arcades along the Essex coast, but instead I decided to spend more time in a single place and build a bigger picture of that environment. Assisted by my producer Nick Woolgar, we visited the

pier over a number of months, from busy bank holiday mornings to dreary weekday evenings. Different people use the pier for different purposes; nostalgia, fun, escapism, mindfulness or even just a free toilet after being on the beach! I thought it important to put the pier in the context of its environment. It offers escapism to a certain type of person – whilst others may get a similar feeling from walking along the beach. It's certainly odd to have so much technology suspended above a huge body of water. I'm fascinated by what the future of arcades and even piers in general hold.

The idea is contained in an unsounded metaphor conjured – as only pure sound CAN conjure – by the act of imagining, which is to say, the fancy that these environments continue to rehearse themselves after the gates and doors are locked at the end of the day, when the power is switched off, the lights go dark and the sounds grow silent. When this happens, things revert, and we imagine the arcade room listening through the night to the whispering or roaring of the eternal sea around it and beneath it. Here, as so often, the continuing sound of water offers a counterpoint to the sound of a room, however we may interpret that term. By the sea or by a river, liquid creates an auditory narrative that flows around man-made space as air and weather envelope a structure or an edifice or a tree. The sounds of water inhabit and define the places where they exist, enabling a dialogue of a continuing performative nature. Once set in motion, these sounds assume an identity, which we may comment upon artistically, or simply observe.

In the Merrick piece, the audio was gathered and later shaped in the studio, and the end result was a piece primarily designed for private listening, but for some sound artists, the place itself offers an opportunity to interact *in situ*. In 2010, London's Somerset House Trust, and Sound and Music co-commissioned and co-produced a work by the sound artist Bill Fontana under the title *River Sounding*. Somerset House is situated on the north bank of the River Thames on the site of a royal palace. It stands half way between – and in sight of – both Westminster Abbey and St Paul's Cathedral, directly opposite the Royal National Theatre. The current building was commenced in 1785, but the original palace was built by the Duke of Somerset in the sixteenth century. As it stands, it is a great quadrangle surrounded by the walls of its stone buildings, today housing a variety of purposes, including the Courtauld Institute of Art. In the river frontage of the building, there is an arch that, before the creation of the Thames Embankment, gave direct access to boats and ships to and from the river. In other words, the Thames once flowed *through and into* Somerset House, and Bill Fontana's sound work returned the river to the building by creating an acoustic journey that became an architectural one.

Describing *River Sounding* at the time of creation, Fontana made a telling statement: 'All sound that we hear is a description of the space it is sounding in' (Fontana, in Fontana et al., p. 14). His work placed river sounds back inside the building, in rooms and spaces which were on the level of the old river, before the creation of the Embankment, namely spaces that were lightwells:

> *River Sounding* is a hybrid sound sculpture that combines a large-scale sonic mapping of the lightwells with a series of discrete video installations in various chambers off these beautiful subterranean passages. A choreographic mix of sound elements I recorded from various locations, from the Thames Estuary to Teddington Lock, is projected into the upper and lower levels of the lightwells using a large-scale multi-channel loudspeaker system. These sound elements are flowing and moving through the lightwells and are audible on the edges of the plaza, mixing with the white noise of the fountains.
>
> *(Ibid.)*

In his 2010 introduction to the piece, John Kieffer, then director of Sound and Music,[2] suggested that this audio visual location-immersed drama occupied a place somewhere between metaphor and fact, something that was neither documentary nor straightforward interpretation:

> By recording and assembling the plaintive sound of whistle buoys, the vibrations of the Millennium Bridge and Kew Bridge Steam Museum, and by transposing them in time and place to Somerset House he makes us, the listener and watcher, do the work.
>
> *(Kieffer, Ibid., p. 3)*

Fontana's installation brought not only distant locations along the Thames, but elements of the remote past beside the present signals of London river life together in one historic location, and in so doing, created 'an immersive journey… that creates many different experiences of place, time, memory and the relationship of the visual to the aural' (Fontana, ibid., p. 15). Just as, however, the North Sea around Walton Pier resumes itself when the holidaymakers have gone home, so at Somerset House, when the commissioned work came to an end, the lights and speakers ended their performance and the building itself – and the river that touched it – continued their duet, within the continuity of time and history, having been commented upon briefly by the present.

The development of sound material as art was essentially twentieth-century in its origins, fuelled by the availability of electro-acoustic sources interacting with physical spaces in a temporal dialogue. As Gascia Ouzounian has pointed out, the full acceptance of this requires a reappraisal of sound's place within the context of art itself:

> The emergence of sound installation art in the second half of the twentieth century reflects fundamental shifts within multiple arenas: conceptions of

space and space-time; the ascendancy of site within the aural imagination; the extension of music and sonic arts into expanded sculptural and architectural models; and the role of the public in relation to aesthetic experience. Perhaps owing to its liminal position between more established disciplines, however, sound installation art remains under-recognised within historical accounts of twentieth-century art and music, even as it marks this history through such shifts, extensions and ruptures.

(Ouzounian, in Born, p. 73)

Ouzounian's reference to 'the role of the public' brings us back to Walton Pier's amusement arcade, and in particular, the participatory nature of the sounds generated within it. The artist may create a work to which the visitor or listener responds, be they in a traditional gallery, a building not normally associated with sound-art installations, or even sitting beside a radio receiver or listening through headphones. In such circumstances, the 'audience' for want of a better word, reacts to sound as an object, albeit a temporal one.

Beyond the Fourth Wall

There are other environments beyond concert halls, where the public response is both communal and participatory. In sporting arenas, be it athletics, tennis, football, rugby or baseball, spectators are themselves part of the spectacle, most notably through their generation of sound. As a listener to a radio relay of such events, we rely almost as much on the location sound with its highs and lows, its climaxes and lulls, as on actual commentary to convey mood, atmosphere and a sense of the dramatic swing of events as they happen. At such events we become used to talking about 'crowds' rather than 'audiences'. It is significant and appropriate, because in such situations, while we may tune in to the second-hand relay as listeners, we attend the happening itself not as listeners but as participants in the action. Many stadia have been appropriated as concert venues, and some of the greatest music events ever have been at such venues as Wembley Stadium, Candlestick Park or Shea Stadium, and key to this is the destruction of the fourth wall that traditionally established a division between performer and audience. A notable example that bridged genres, time and audience/crowd was during the build-up to the 1990 football World Cup finals in Italy, when six thousand people came to the Roman Baths of Caracalla, dating from 212 and 216 AD, to hear Luciano Pavarotti, Placido Domingo and Jose Carreras perform. A similar event occurred at the 1994 World Cup, when 56,000 people attended a concert by the same singers in the Dodger Stadium in Los Angeles, an event watched on television by 1.3 billion viewers. Who can forget Freddie Mercury of the rock band Queen sharing a duet with audiences of 100,000 people, playing the crowd in a way that made the performance for many, definitive?

For the most part, when employed in their traditional roles, sporting arenas are better known for generating sound rather than listening to it, although a disinterested observer attending a match by the Welsh national rugby team, would without doubt understand the intimidation to the opposition of thousands of partisan voices raised in excitement, triumph, anger or song; To hear 'Land of My Fathers' sung by 60,000 voices is something long remembered. As a boy, I recall attending matches at Bramall Lane, the home ground of Sheffield United FC. At that time, during the 1950s, the pitch had crowd stands on only three sides, because the club shared the area with Yorkshire County Cricket Club, and during the football season, matches were played against the backdrop of a wide expanse of open grass, with a cricket pavilion in the distance. In 1975, a new stand was added, enclosing the soccer pitch, and thus changing the acoustic properties dramatically. At the same time, with the introduction of all-seat stadia, crowd numbers have reduced greatly, and the atmosphere at matches, including the vocal responses and interaction of crowds, is very different. Fewer voices, but perhaps more aggression. It all has echoes of past times, past civilisations; Greeks and Romans had great amphitheatres, but Rome also had its Colosseum, where blood and death formed the focus of the sport. We may visit the ruins, see them as venerable and thought-provoking, but we must also remain cognisant of the fact that there was a mind behind their construction in the first place, with an eye – and an ear – on cause and effect. Part of the essence of any live performance or entertainment in the broadest sense of a public event, be it a symphony concert, a jazz trio, a sound installation or a sporting spectacle, is the unpredictability of the living space itself.

Another Musician

Taking this to an extreme, the fact that there appears to be nothing happening in any particular room, does not reduce the performative nature of any sonic events that happen there. No two performances of Bill Fontana's Somerset House work were the same, because the air that transmitted the sounds also carried serendipitous signals of the fluctuating river and London's presence going on around the building. Such accidents can carry new layers of meaning to the mind, as chance makes associations possible. A performance space is, in the end, a place where a performance takes place, whether the room was designed for this specific purpose or not. The performance may constitute structured music, speech or sound in the conventional sense, or a form of duet between human agencies and the place itself. In 1976, the flautist Paul Horn made a remarkable series of recordings inside the Great Pyramid of Giza in Egypt, in the form of a number of improvisations taped in various chambers. Recordings were made in the evenings, when the structure was closed to visitors, and what is most noticeable is the resonance for which the rooms are famous. In the King's Chamber of the Cheops Pyramid, for example, there is a sense that the space is much larger than the approximate 34 x 17 x 19 feet dimensions. In the opening recording, Horn began by hitting a large granite sarcophagus in the centre of the room with the flat of his hand, which emits a resonant tone of 438 Hz, slightly lower than an A. He then tuned his flute to that and improvised from there:

> Sitting on the floor in front of the coffer with a stereo mic in the centre of the room, I began to play, choosing the alto flute to begin with. The echo [*sic*] was wonderful, about eight seconds. The chamber responded to every note equally. I waited for the echo to decay and then played again. Groups of notes would suspend and all come back as a chord. Sometimes certain notes would stick out more than others. It was always changing. I just listened and responded as if I were playing with another musician.[3]

Horn and his recording team then moved to the head of what is known as The Grand Gallery within the Pyramid, which had been reported to have unusual acoustic properties. To Horn's surprise, 'it was very dead sounding', all the more remarkable, given its length of more than 156 feet. There was, however, a reverberation, an echo from the King's Chamber, 'going out in the Grand Gallery, bouncing off the walls and coming back through the anti-chamber and into the King's Chamber' (ibid.). It is in the King's Chamber recordings that there is the strongest sense of an almost living acoustic within the structure, a quality that Horn's instrument awakens. The recordings also evoke a strong imaginative pictorial sense in the listening mind: musician and sound recordist, surrounded by the candlelit walls of the chamber, and the man-made notes hanging in clusters around them as the chamber remembered music.

Sometimes temporal circumstances within a space make their own narrative. During a field recording in Harlech Castle, on the west coast of Wales, I found myself witness to a chilling example of this. I had been recording in the north-eastern gate house tower of the castle, a narrow cylinder of a structure, circular and several hundred feet high. It had once been punctuated by several floors, but these are gone now, and the tower is open to the elements. As I recorded, rooks argued somewhere above me out of sight, a cold wind funnelled down, and a light rain began to fall. The place is a tourist hotspot, but today it was quiet, only a few visitors braving the late October weather, so I had the luxury of letting the sound speak for itself. The castle has a long and bloody history; built by Edward 1 during his invasion of Wales between 1282 and 1289, over several centuries it played its part in several wars, and withstood a number of violent sieges. From 1404 for a number of years, it was the residence and military headquarters of Owain Glyndŵr until it was recaptured by English forces in 1409. Glyndŵr was a Welsh leader who instigated an ultimately unsuccessful war of independence with the aim of ending English rule. After his time, Harlech continued to be a stronghold for numerous military interests. It was held by the Lancastrians for seven years during the Wars of the Roses, until the Yorkist troops forced its surrender in 1468. During the English Civil War, Harlech was the last stronghold of the Royalists to fall, in 1647 to the

Parliamentary army. The visitor cannot but think about this long violent past; to stand alone in the ruins of this place on a bleak day, it is hard not to imagine what it has seen and heard. Wars, wars, wars: the mind plays a collage of stories at such times, and I was no exception, listening to the wind through the gaping windows, sounding like a sonic cliché of all the eerie winds I'd ever heard on drama sound effects recordings. The place WAS its own drama. Then, without warning, the sound changed. At first, I thought it was a strange new version of the wind, then as it grew in volume and intensity, I realised this was a twenty-first-century intrusion. It reached a crescendo, all-enveloping, deafening, amplified down the tower, assaulting my recorder, so I saw the input levels rush off the scale and distort. Then it was gone, as quickly as it had come. The source never revealed itself visually, but the sound was unmistakably that of a Eurofighter Typhoon combat aircraft, undergoing low-flying exercises around the mountains of Snowdonia. Circumstances and location had left me tuned and receptive to all suggestions and associative ideas, and this seemed a particularly eloquent expression of irony; castles may crumble, weapons may change, but the intentions remain. We continue to wage wars. Events for me had taken an unexpected turn; an historical drama had suddenly become highly current, and the room presented me with a form of live improvised audio theatre that sent me home in a reflective mood.

Notes

1 Extracts from an interview with Frazer Merrick, reproduced with permission.
2 Sound and Music is the UK's national agency for new music, established in October 2008. *River Sounding* by Bill Fontana was one of its early commissions.
3 Paul Horn, liner note from CD: *Inside the Great Pyramid*. Kuckuck Records: 12060–2. Original vinyl album issued 1976, CD with additional material issued 1991.

References

Clarke, Eric F. 'Music, Space and Subjectivity', in Georgina Born, *Music, Sound and Space: Transformations of Public and Private Experience*. Cambridge: Cambridge University Press, 2013, pp. 73–89.

Fontana, Bill. River Sounding. London: Somerset House Trust/Sound and Music, 2010.

Gann, Kyle. *No Such Thing as Silence: John Cage's 4' 33"*. New York: Yale University Press, 2010.

Godwin, Joscelyn. *Athanasius Kircher's Theatre of the World: His Life, Work, and the Search for Universal Knowledge*. Rochester, VT: Inner Traditions, 2009.

Howard, Deborah, and Moretti, Laura. *Sound and Space in Renaissance Venice*. New Haven, CT: Yale University Press, 2009.

Jaffe, Christopher J. *The Acoustics of Performance Halls: Spaces for Music from Carnegie Hall to the Hollywood Bowl*. New York: W.W. Norton & Company, 2010.

Maekawa, Z., Rindel, J.H. and Lord, P. *Environmental and Architectural Acoustics*. Boca Raton, FL: CRC Press, 2019.

Ouzounian, Gascia. 'Sound Installation Art: From Spatial Poetics to Politics, Aesthetics to Ethics', in Georgina Born, *Music, Sound and Space: Transformations of Public and Private Experience*. Cambridge: Cambridge University Press, 2013, pp. 73–89.

Stocker, Michael. *Hear Where We Are: Sound, Ecology and Sense of Place*. New York: Springer, 2013.

Toop, David. *Ocean of Sound: Aether Talk, Ambient Sound and Imaginary Worlds*. London: Serpent's Tail, 1995.

Vitruvius. Trans. Morris Hicky Morgan. *The Ten Books on Architecture*. New York: Dover Editions, 2015.

4

THE SOUND OF A ROOM AT PRAYER

Choirs of Angels

Every structure of mankind – from Stonehenge to the newest, brightest mirror-glass skyscraper – has been designed, built, made, constructed and laboured over. But there comes a time when the builders leave, and the building itself settles into its own being, beginning its journey through time like a newly launched ship. We may imagine it then, in newly enclosed stillness, awaiting its first sonic interaction. The Finnish architect Julhani Pallasmaa wrote that

> architecture presents the drama of construction silenced into matter, space and light. Ultimately, architecture is the art of petrified silence. When the clutter of construction work ceases, and the shouting of workers dies away, a building becomes a museum of waiting, patient silence.
>
> *(Pallasmaa, p. 55)*

Yet beneath it, as has been suggested, there lies somewhere that strange indefinable tone, that mystery that Peter Zumthor spoke of in the first chapter of this book. If I listen long enough to the presence held in the space between things, be those things walls or horizons, if I concentrate and focus, I may hear something.

For the tourist or worshipper, the approach to Lincoln Cathedral is the perfect warm-up for the main event. The church stands on a high hill, overlooking the city and enfolded by narrow streets with a busy sense that this is how it has always been. Beyond that, the three great towers dominate the skyline for many miles. I remember once standing on the summit of the tower of St Botolph's Church, Boston – 'the Boston Stump'– and seeing through the haze, the distant shape of Lincoln, 27 miles away as the crow flies, but even at that range, awe-inspiring. Yet my first visit to Lincoln Cathedral began with an unexpected twist. Coming to the main entrance at the front of the church, we were told that a service was under way in the main part, and we could either stay outside until it finished, or enter at the rear of the building and wait there. We chose the latter, and were led round to a small door on the south side of the huge edifice. I remember coming into what is known as The Angel Choir. Lincoln Cathedral has endured fire (1141) and earthquake (1185), and much of what the visitor sees now dates from the restoration after these events. The Angel Choir is appropriate as a title; completed in 1280, it is named for the twenty-eight carved angels that adorn it. The great East Window, the largest and earliest eight-light window in England, floods the space with coloured light, making the stone floor glow. On my first visit, however, I did not initially take in these things. What I walked into was not so much a physical space, as pure enveloping sound. The service was going on in the main body of the building beyond screens of wood and stone; the cathedral choir was singing an anthem, and it rang through the church from the space we could not see, rising into the roof, weaving through intricacies of stonework, reverberating, echoing and resonating on every surface and flowing into each crevice. The walls gave it back, pouring it down and around us as we remained transfixed, surrounded by visible and invisible angels. It was a transcendent moment, no more than five minutes, I imagine (I have no measure for the passage of time during this event) but a period in which as the song occurred – and since in memory – the building that is Lincoln Cathedral actually seemed to be translated into pure sound.

The great places of worship wherever they may be in the world possess this capacity to create a sense that they are musical instruments, or at least divine sounding boards in which sonic presences may be transmuted into another existence. This is perhaps one example of what it means to have 'a religious experience'. I have to remind myself that the fabric and shape that made this sound possible comes from the hand of man, remade after fire and the shifting of the turbulent earth, fashioned into the walls surrounding this space in which soprano voices soar like birds in a wide blue sky. After the music ended, and the service came to its conclusion, we were admitted to the main part of the church, I remember walking around in a daze. A man approached me: 'Are you alright? You seem to be emerging from a trance!' I tried to express the happening, of coming in, expecting a visual spectacle, but being overtaken and surrounded by sound. I turned to him, and saw he was a member of the clergy. 'I know', he said, 'I've been here for thirty years, and it still has that effect on me'. It was sound augmented by the shape and structure and consistency of stone. Later, when I had time to reflect on it, I found myself remembering the early pages of William Golding's great novel *The Spire*, in which Jocelin, the medieval dean of a cathedral (in Golding's case, Salisbury) dreams of adding a 400-foot spire to the existing building, even though it lacks adequate foundations and no one has ever built this high before. The sheer weight, height and scale of these great churches are evidence of extraordinary acts of faith, and among the first rewards to those early builders must have been the sound they created by enclosing the air of that place in stone. Even as Lincoln was rising from its foundations, or the workmen toiled at the post-fire and earthquake reconstruction, the sacred sounds flowed and grew. Golding describes it perfectly in his novel: a time at Salisbury when worship and utilitarian work went on side by side, blending into the song of a place being born.

> He lifted the latch carefully so as not to make a noise… But even as he stepped inside, he knew that his caution was unnecessary, since there was a whole confusion of noise in the cathedral already. Matins, diminished, its sounds so small they might be held in one hand, was nonetheless audible from the Lady Chapel at the other end of the cathedral, beyond the wood and canvas screen. There was a nearer sound that told – though the components were so mixed by echo as to be part of each other – that men were digging in earth and stone. They were talking, ordering, shouting sometimes, dragging wood across pavement, wheeling and dropping loads, then throwing them roughly into place, so that the total noise would have been formless as the noises of the market place, had not the echoing spaces made it chase round and round so that it caught up with itself and the shrill choir, and sang endlessly on one note. The noises were so new, that he hurried to the centre line of the cathedral in the shadow of the great west door, genuflected to the hidden High Altar; and then stood, looking.
>
> (Golding, p. 9)

Golding describes layers of sound. We listen to the world through such layers, and focus on what we are required to know, understand or enjoy at any one moment. It is when the ear is surprised by sound, as when I entered through that small south door, when we become overwhelmed by sound, the source of which we cannot see, and which for even a brief moment is mysterious to us, that awe, wonder or even terror strikes us. The capacity of giant churches to offer sound from beyond immediate space, from as it were, from the other side of a veil, makes such moments timeless. When I arrived home after my visit, I sought out a recording of the anthem I had heard that day, and played it in great anticipation. It was a piece by a contemporary composer, and it was as beautiful as I remembered. Yet it was somehow a disappointment, leaving me strangely unmoved. Everything about it was right: the voices, the tempo, and the mood. The piece was even conducted by the composer, so I should have accepted it as definitive. What it lacked was Lincoln Cathedral's voice, the vast resonating chamber of the place itself. Every great church has its own voice, the sound built into it. Writing in 1939 of Strasbourg Cathedral, Paul Claudel noted that

> the great empty spaces… have as their role only the modelling of the invisible about us, the circumscribing of the volume of air and of thought for

our nourishment, this breath that God places at our disposal to draw on, to transform into word and song.

(Claudel, p. 202)

Whether, as Claudel suggests, such spaces contain some kind of spiritual presence depends upon the religious persuasions of each individual. On the other hand, I have made recordings in spaces that are equally vast, that, even in near silence, possess very different qualities. The approach to St Pancras International Station from London's Euston Road suggests a cross between a cathedral and a Disney castle. Once inside, the vast arc of the roof over the lines and platforms is redolent of a past glory-time of steam trains. Occasionally, the slumbering Eurostar trains awaiting their next mission let out a hiss from their airbrakes that to the mind of a certain age might conjure the ghost of a long-gone steam engine. Otherwise, my recording gives little away of the purpose of the space. Could I be in a huge church? The delay of sound around the curve of the roof tells me I am in a great room with hard surfaces and huge volumes of contained air. Yet the sound somehow remains more industrial than sacred, more utilitarian than supernatural. If a choir performed a motet by Thomas Tallis in this space, would the music transform it, turn a railway station into a church? As Trevor Cox has reminded us, the sonic qualities of churches are deliberately associated with spirituality:

> The excessive reverberation forces the congregation into silence or hushed whispers, because otherwise speech is rapidly amplified by reflections and creates an ungodly cacophony. During services, the music and words appear to wrap around you like the omnipresent God being worshipped. The acoustics have also influenced services, as the use of chanting and the slow liturgical voice counters the muddy speech in such reverberant spaces.
>
> *(Cox, p. 42)*

Composers who write for such acoustics understand this perfectly. The English composer Ralph Vaughan Williams composed his *Fantasia on a Theme of Thomas Tallis* in 1910 and conducted its first performance in Gloucester Cathedral as part of the Three Choirs Festival of that year. It is sound full of long notes, ethereal sonorities and rich textures, played by a string orchestra with a string quartet at its heart, like a sonic cathedral with a small chapel contained within it. Vaughan Williams set the quartet apart physically from the rest of the players, so some of the sound comes as if from another realm entirely, unseen and haunting. It is a composition that uses the building – the acoustic and the spatial presence itself – as players in the orchestra, alongside the visible musicians. Vaughan Williams deliberately designed a configuration that resembles the characteristics of an organ, but the Tudor polyphony that lies at the heart of the work grew out of the great and ancient English cathedral tradition; countless composers have understood that in such environments, different rules must apply; short, sharp staccato notes destroy themselves, just as someone speaking too quickly becomes overrun by the delay and decay of sound around them. The Austrian romantic composer Anton Bruckner was long misunderstood and ridiculed by some for the abrupt long pauses in his huge symphonies. Bruckner learned his craft as a church organist, and he wrote for the acoustics of giant churches. Listening to his music played in a church therefore offers a feeling that the building lends its voice to the sound, as the music gives itself to the silence out of which it came. Musicians and building become one, like the components of a giant bell in which stillness is the property at its heart. Thus, the room in which the music sounds, completes the sense of it, and contributes to its meaning.

Might the enormous space of St Pancras lend itself to that? A train was leaving, the sound was deafening as the engines started up and the machine pulled away towards France, leaving behind a relieved ambience of relative quiet. What would Bruckner make of it if he were invited to play one of his organ improvisations here? There is more to sonic spirituality than sheer size, or even the pure science of acoustics. As Knight points out, there are other factors – sensory and associative – that affect what we hear and how we absorb it:

> Religious music performed within religious spaces can take on an added dimension that is hard to replicate in a concert hall. The presence of the divine, in sanctified space, may have meaning far beyond what a sceptic is able to deal with, and the inner message and power of sacred music, even when performed in such a space but apart from a service, may speak to the audience in ways that are hard to explain.
>
> *(Knight, p. 176)*

I hold a memory of a choral concert in Notre Dame Cathedral, Paris in May 1967 of Fauré's *Requiem* and Bruckner's *Te Deum*. I knew both works very well, and had attended a number of live performances; on this occasion, however, it was the building that was the key performer. Fifty-two years later, I was sitting in a motorway hotel room somewhere between London and Liverpool, on my way home, and that evening, turned the television on to see Notre Dame in flames. Like millions around the world, I sat transfixed with horror and sadness; then in my mind, I heard the last bars of the Bruckner, where the full choir and orchestra thunder towards the work's majestic conclusion. I could still hear the sound dissolve into silence, melting through the arches and chapels, the statues and stone crevices of the building, all of which contributed to the sound; and I pictured my young self sitting near the back, in one of the cheaper seats behind a pillar, and somehow by my very presence, insignificant as it was, playing a minute part in how that room sounded on that particular evening. I thought of what had happened to the place, and what would happen now. No matter how lovingly any building is restored, it is by the very act of that restoration, changed, and however subtly, part of that change must be its sound. I have a recording of that evening's concert, but even without it, I have carried for more than half a century the moment when the human sound of Anton Bruckner ended and the building sang on for a few precious, sacred seconds.

Aural Architecture

This book is about the sounds that places bring to us, and we know a place is reactive, just as a sound requires a space in which to be heard. At the same time, our underlying interest here is with the sound or sounds generated independently of other forces, by the immediate environment itself. The common link is air, permitting audibility. Before it can have significance, sound must be heard, and the most demonstrative of sounds within a location, affecting atmosphere, space and our personal responses to both place and self, is music. It is, as Clarke confirms, 'inextricably bound up with the wider auditory world, since it sounds within it, incorporates environmental sounds into its own material, and takes on fluid relationships with the physical and social spaces that it occupies' (Clarke, , p. 90). Among the most emotive and suggestive of such spaces are sacred edifices of any religion, because as well as being social acoustic spaces, they also provide textual association with a purpose and message beyond the physical, while employing and exploiting the senses for their broader purpose. These are indeed performance spaces, but here as perhaps in few other environments, the place itself, as I suggested in the previous chapter, is the performer almost as much as the human forces within it. When we consider the wealth of music created as a voice for religion, from plainchant to the arcing sonorities of John Taverner, Alessandro Striggio or Thomas Tallis, we come to a poignant thought: the weaving of Tudor polyphony, the long soaring notes of soprano voices and the angelic harmonies of church choirs are more than expressions of faith, they are partners to the great buildings they were written for. It was Goethe who wrote, 'I call architecture "petrified music"' (Howard and Moretti, p. 8) and Pevsner who said 'a bicycle shed is a building; Lincoln Cathedral is a piece of architecture' (Pevsner, quoted in Hendrix, p. 71). We need to follow these two statements and connect them, because there are other criteria and motivations at work here other than a construction industry, of whatever historical period, and the initiation of ideas that lead ultimately to a physical or abstract work of art is both mysterious and crucial in how human expression interacts with a space, with the enclosed air that personalises and characterises the sound of a particular place. John Shannon Hendrix has usefully developed Pevsner's aphorism:

> Pevsner's criterion for a building as architecture was that the forms of the building were combined with the forms of the other arts: sculpture, painting, and stained glass, so that the building would be a representation of the aspirations of its culture. A building is architecture if it expresses an idea

external to the forms of the building itself, the idea being a philosophical or epistemological structure.

(*Hendrix, p. 71*)

The conclusion to be taken from Hendrix's statement comes from what is missing from it: music and voice. In terms of the age of great cathedral building, the architects had terms of reference drawn from the arts, crafts and philosophies prevalent at the time, and their churches were reflections of this. In turn, the sonic product and expression of these physical creations found itself inspired to articulate what its authors saw in terms of a new music that both utilised the places themselves and created an auralisation of them. In so doing, this sound both shared a voice with the architecture, and created a sonic extension of the faith and philosophy that had driven the building of the very walls themselves in the first place. Once, someone must have walked into a space like Lincoln Cathedral for the first time and listened. If that person was a musician, they would have had a particular kind of response, and out of that response, ultimately, came the kind of music that seems to be so much a part of the place itself. In other words, the building was here first, a kind of silent music that required itself to be given a voice as a further expression of its purpose. The sounds of interweaving voices in Tudor Polyphony were extensions of the ornament and soaring space that the faithful saw around them. It did not – could not – exist until the thinking that informed the shapes of Gothic architecture provided a studio in which to sound. A churchgoer saw statues of angels; the music gave those angels voices, disguising mortal breathing in a web of ethereal sound within a tracery of the 'petrified music' of stone. Yet it is about more than sound, and it is about more than religious faith: it is an expression of both, growing from philosophical thinking. It is our loss if we separate effect and cause:

> The forms of the cathedral are a visual and structural model of the way people thought in that period, in terms of philosophy and theology, and the organisation of all forms of cultural production. The forms of the cathedral tell us how the people of the culture understood the structure of the cosmos, the relation between the human being and the world, and the relation between faith and reason. The cathedral has a metaphysical structure as well as a physical structure, and the cathedral can be called architecture if architecture is taken to be an art, expressing an idea, in the Platonic sense, as separate from the material itself.
>
> (*Ibid., pp. 71–2*)

Thus every sonically inspirational place has a kinship between its poetic and spiritual essence, the motive behind its creation, and a dynamic human need to physically interpret the philosophy that underpins it. We might even suggest that all churches remain unfinished until a human voice sings the first note. The creation of a room, the size, shape and the fabric with which it is constructed, obviously dictates how it will sound. Yet by enclosing air, we create some accidental sonic events, or rather the potential for them to occur. Listening to an old radio, I hear the voice or the music through the flowing of atmospherics. Sometimes these sounds intrude, but at others, they may become a part in my mind of the source's identity. I remember listening to a particular sports commentator this way. I became familiar with the overall sound, so much so that, one day, when I heard his voice coming through a clear DAB transmission, it somehow did not seem right. Atmospherics, be they in electronic devices, or held within the space of a performance space of any kind, are part of the aural experience. This explains my sense of dissatisfaction on listening to the choral anthem I had first heard, unseen in Lincoln, within a studio recording context. A landscape may inspire a sonic response, but a room partners it in an interactive way that is both physical and abstract. As Blesser and Salter put it:

> Just as light sources are required to illuminate visual architecture, so sound sources (sonic events) are required to "illuminate" aural architecture in order to make it aurally perceptible… Aural architecture requires the presence of sound sources to illuminate the space, and a soundscape is also the same combination of space and sources. What then is the difference between them? With a soundscape, the sounds are important in themselves, as for example, birds singing or people talking, whereas with aural architecture, those same sounds serve only to illuminate it. The personality of a soundscape includes the personality of sounds as well as the personality of the aural architecture illuminated by those sounds. Aural architecture emphasises sound primarily as illumination, whereas a soundscape emphasises sound in itself. The distinction is subtle…
>
> *(Blesser and Salter, pp. 15–16)*

While Blesser and Salter are correct, I might underline that the ever-present ambience within the room provides the common denominator of a subtle sound bed for all other sonic events that occur within it. In such circumstances, the speaker, singer or musician has no choice but to move to the rhythm and pace of the building itself, to articulate thoughts and feelings in partnership and in time with the architecture. We find ourselves led towards metaphysics. Yet science has demonstrated that the sonic presence of sacred space CAN be replicated. The acoustic of the great Hagia Sophia in Istanbul has long been legendary, from its time as a Greek Orthodox Cathedral for nearly five hundred years, between the fifth and fifteenth century. In this example, researchers from Stanford University, recording the acoustic of the building and then, as it were, wrapping it around singers who performed in Stanford's Bing concert hall, have by way of experiment recreated it artificially. The effect was as far as it may be possible, a facsimile of the oral/aural experience of a medieval act of worship. I have touched on this in my book *The Sound Inside the Silence* (pp. 85–6). While this examines the techniques surrounding the sound, it is important to understand that such places as the Hagia Sophia have a connection with sound that is beyond anything that can be reproduced – however technically accurate – elsewhere. While a building may be appropriated by other religions, or even deconsecrated, it will, within its original structure, remain faithful to the motives behind its aural origins. As Pentcheva has reminded us, it is crucial to remember 'the sonic aspect of the Byzantine "image of God" and its performative nonrepresentational character' (Pentcheva, p. 11). Architecture is multi-sensory, and a sound from a human source becomes transformed, and one might say 'owned', by an acoustic, a transitory part of the very building itself.

> The vast interior volume and reflective materials of Hagia Sophia produce reverberant acoustics, enabling a single note exhaled in space to last more than ten seconds. This resonant chamber dissolves the intelligibility of speech but enhances melismatic chant. The aurality of Hagia Sophia presents alternative, nontextual evidence that can expand our access to the Byzantine "experience" of sacred space.
>
> *(Ibid.)*

The building itself is the text, both visually and in sonic terms. As Howard and Moretti have argued regarding the sacred spaces of renaissance Venice, 'serious attention must be given to the ways in which the worshipper or spectator combines aural and visual sensations' (Howard and Moretti, p. 5). If one were to speak of a 'sensory assault' in such places, it might seem somehow inappropriate. Yet

> a magnificent state ritual involving hundreds of participants in sumptuous robes, performed under the glittering domes of San Marco [for example] could predispose the listener to detect magnificent qualities in the music. Sound cannot be easily subtracted from ceremonial events.

Perhaps here lies another factor in my Lincoln experience. To this, one should add that a building may have the capacity to do more than simply enhance sound. As long resonance times meld and blend harmonies, the architecture may actually create its own non-human music, while making, as we have seen, the intelligibility of the spoken word more problematic, and so heightening the impression of an ethereal presence within music that subjugates the human. Palladio and the other architects of the acoustics of Venetian churches understood and acknowledged Vitruvius, as would their successors, in the necessity of absorbing the key differing factors involved in building for the spoken or sung word. The introduction of cornices in order to reflect sound back down into interiors, a major consideration when speech rather than song was the primary consideration, as for example in debating chambers. 'When the walls are encircled by cornices, the voice, as it rises from below, will be delayed before it carries upward on the air and dissipates; it will be intelligible to the ears' (Vitruvius, p. 65). The advent of polyphonic choral music in the seventeenth century raised issues of clarity or merging of sounds that required clearer, less reverberant acoustics than had pertained previously. Too many sonic signals overlapping destroys meaning, and can be disorientating. On the other hand, 'reverberation makes sensorially accessible the interaction between animate and inanimate' (Pentcheva, p. 119), providing a link between the physical and spiritual that for many lies at the heart of performed religious ritual. Invariably, sacred music, specifically to be performed as part of the liturgy, or as complementary to it, was by its very nature, textual in origin. The masses of Byrd or Taverner are sung in Latin, which presupposes an understanding of the sacred message. Yet within the liquid acoustics of a resonating sacred space, the actual words may be unintelligible, and to many a modern listener, perhaps even incomprehensible. We are left with words as sounds, and a purely sonic effect in which the music becomes an abstract expression of a time, place and mood. A printed text would help if the congregation was literate, but timbre, texture and space would have been the elements that communicated in such situations, and in absorbing the sensory experience above all else, taking the message beyond the cerebral and into a purely emotional event that was both external and internal. In other words, to a non-Tudor ear and mind, the meaning has become overtaken by the medium, and we bask in its colour, shape and modulations, as we would allow a renaissance painting to affect us. There may well be a message, an allegory or teaching going on, but it does not concern us in terms of our immediate reaction to what we are hearing. What matters as we listen, is feeling, and engaging with something on the other side of thought.

Answering Voices

There may be another aspect to the transcendent power of sung sound in such giant spaces. As Clarke has pointed out, 'the localisation of sound sources can be reduced to the detection of distance and direction, perceived and expressed in terms of three dimensions of space in relation to an observer' (Clarke, p. 92). The two factors that most enable us to understand the directional nature of a sound are time and intensity, relative to the acoustical signal as it reaches the two ears.

> A sound source to the left of an observer will give rise to a positive intensity in the left ear (due to the "shadowing" effect of the head for the right ear) and the waveform will reach the left ear marginally before it reaches the right ear. It is the detection of this Interaural Level Difference (ILD) and Interaural Time Difference (ITD) that specifies the position of a sound source for the listener.
>
> *(Ibid.)*

Bregman reminds us: 'if the auditory system is to group sounds by their locations, it must have a method for representing locations on some sort of continuum' (Bregman, p. 73). In some large spaces, such perceptions may become confused. The nature of the architecture – domes, arches, statues, cornices, buttresses and so on, may – deliberately or accidentally – undermine our sense of aural direction, creating an almost hallucinogenic effect at times, and defying us to identify from whence the sound is actually emanating. It is all-surrounding and enveloping, heightening the sense of the spiritual experience and for some seemingly suggesting the presence of a non-human entity in sound, independent of any physically identifiable sonic source.

In Chapter 7, I would like to explore something of the ancient and fundamental origins of our relationship with special sound, and one might almost say, the *need* for answering resonances within the human mind, the sense of confirmation of our existence it brings. The work of Iegor Reznikoff in European Palaeolithic painted caves underlines, this, and for Reznikoff himself it has opened up personal meanings within the interiors of Christian churches:

> Concerning the relationship with the Invisible through sound and paintings, as in Palaeolithic ornate caves, the following it is worth telling. Some years ago, I gave a concert in the *Basilica Superiore* in Assisi, which is decorated with the famous frescos by Giotto, Cimabue and others; I was singing some grand solo chants of Christian Antiquity. In the middle of a chant, I couldn't stop contemplating one of those frescos, and suddenly I was seized by the great impression that came from the paintings and the painted glasses, by the architecture, by the fact that under my feet, in the *Basilica Inferiore*, is the grave of St Francesco, and by the marvel of the resonance of the church, it was as if the frescos were animated, the whole church was singing. The emotion given by this extraordinary relation with the Invisible was so strong that, for a short while, I had to stop singing. Truly this was sacred art. As in Palaeolithic ornate caves, paintings, sounds, resonance and the whole space of the Basilica were linked together in high praise to the Invisible.
>
> *(Reznikoff, 2. 9)*

This sense of the visible linking to the invisible, physical expressions of intangible elements, is strongly rooted in sound's relationship to sacred architecture, but also to many other forms of art, as for example in the philosophy behind the work of painters such as Wassily Kandinsky and, particularly, Paul Klee, to whom I will return in the final chapter of this book. The partnership between a sound and a space can also provoke internal neurological responses that are beyond their sonic origins, stimulating associative ideas that may be symbolic or metaphorical. Time and history play their part, and because sound is temporal itself, there is an extra power in sound moving through an ancient space. 'Because sound… mediates the relationship of the person to the environment, it is only a simple additional step for it to come to symbolise that relationship' (Truax, p. 72). Sound that encircles and envelopes us as we stand and look up at carved angels gazing down at us, seems not only to emanate from the angels themselves, but to evoke the heavenly world they inhabit. The fact that this has in some cases occurred to thousands of other witnesses over centuries in this very place adds its own sense of veracity to the experience. 'When such symbolisms function for countless people over the centuries in many different contexts, the symbol acquires the richness and abstractness of the archetype, with its power to find expression in countless specific instances' (Ibid.). It is above all a dialogue with the self, within each individual, whatever the religion, a confirmation within a public space of a deeply personal interpretation of meaning. If the visual enhances the sonic and vice versa, dramatising symbols that suggest meaning around us, we also as participants come bearing metaphors: 'The pattern recognised in an aural image can often be compared to other patterns which it can then come to represent'. In places of communal experience, notably and powerfully, places such as churches and mosques, internal, personal and individual associations can feed off 'the layers of meaning that sound can have within the acoustic community' (Ibid.). A moment of transcendent spirituality in such an environment is one in which the community itself plays a key role, surrounding the individual with an apparently confirmatory presence that unites personal experience with the surround sound and ambience of the place itself. Bohlman has written that 'the architecture of European mosques and synagogues bore witness to the rise of public religion' within their very architectural construction.

> Both mosques and synagogues' arabesque aestheticised the orientation of worship towards the East (Mecca and Jerusalem), whereas minarets served as symbols of soundscapes that ritually gathered worshippers to pray together and participate in the common auditory experience of listening to Qur'an and Torah recitation... the transformation of the synagogue and the mosque, therefore, was critically about the sound of worship and music, above all, the enhancement of their audibility in the spaces of public religion.
>
> *(Bohlman, pp. 210–11)*

Crucially, 'public religion is the space of the private that is opened through music, coming from outside-in' (ibid., p. 212). It is a visible space made audible, an externalisation of required internal impulses of the human. Furthermore, reverberant acoustics 'transform human voices into that luminous, unintelligible sonic emanation that frees itself from the flow of information, escaping the shackles of human speech' (Pentcheva, p. 119). It is almost akin to liquid, hence my sense that in Lincoln Cathedral, the song was actually *becoming* the building, flowing into all its crevices and filling the space. As Murray Schafer says, in answer to his own question, 'what was the first sound heard? It was the caress of the waters' (Murray Schafer, p. 15). The Kingdom of God, it would seem, is indeed sonically within us.

> The ocean of our ancestors is reproduced in the watery womb of our mother and is chemically related to it. Ocean and Mother. In the dark liquid of ocean the relentless masses of water pushed past the first sonar ear. As the ear of the foetus turns in its amniotic fluid, it too is tuned to the lap and gurgle of water.
>
> *(Ibid.)*

In such buildings as the Hagia Sophia, San Marco or Lincoln, the visitor bathes in seemingly liquid sound, with a sense almost of being once more returned to the womb, while at the same time enveloped in space that seems eternal. The sound of sacred places seeks to be transcendent, to mirror the visual wonders of the architecture that contains it, to invite us to float upwards with it towards heaven. In 1968, when the flautist Paul Horn recorded in the Taj Mahal, he found that the dome of the tomb chamber held the tone for almost half a minute:

> I was using my alto flute, and the low C just flew out and filled the entire room, and just hung there... It was the most beautiful thing I ever heard in my life. I began playing whatever came into my head. I'd let the notes hang there. I could play whole chords and they came back sounding like a chorus of angels. Then I'd play my next phrase on top of that. There was a whole orchestra invisibly suspended in the obscurity of the dome.
>
> *(Horn, CD insert note, Inside the Taj Mahal)*[1]

When Shah Jahan commissioned the Taj as the tomb for his beloved wife, Mumtaz Mahal, in 1632, he had insisted that every element should evoke eternity, and not least of these was the sound. For centuries the place has held this presence, unlocked by a voice or a breath through a flute, to be transformed into 'a chorus of angels'. At one point in the recording, there is heard the sound of an explosion outside the building. A celebration was going on at the time, and fireworks were igniting. This too seems to have been absorbed by the acoustic, with Horn's music, as if the building was making use of sonic raw material, owning it and moulding it to its own aural shape.

Yet a space may contain an aural sense of the sacred even in near silence. For Quakers, who worship without sound, there is no specific sonic design of a room that enhances the experience. Quakers brings their own sound of silence to each space in which they worship. Next to the café and bookshop at their headquarters in Euston Road, London, there is a perfectly circular meeting room. It has a sense of stillness and peace within it that does not exclude the murmur of voices outside, or the rumble of traffic of central London. At the same time, such places may be changed themselves over time by the intensity of feelings that revolve within them. It is in the nature of faith that everyone carries their own response to a place and a time of worship, and each individual may bring a range of place memories that offer comparisons. In answer to my question relating to this, a Quaker friend, Andy Stoller, shared a recollection with regard to a particular location that is germane to this discussion; her reply is significant, citing as she does, one specific meeting room that for her has proved particularly memorable:

> The Quiet Room at Woodbrooke, the Quaker Adult Education College in Birmingham, is a very special oak-panelled room overlooking beautiful grounds. It has a deep sense of peace and spirituality and has been used for Quaker prayer and learning since about 1908. Meeting for Worship is inevitably deeper there before it even starts. You can sense the profoundness of the silence in worship and feel it get deeper maybe for just a minute or so at a time. There is a gathered stillness and a feeling of being 'centred' that I have not felt anywhere else. Things happen from this place, there is an impact on people's lives which is beyond understanding.[2]

The sound of a room may sometimes extend into vibrations, ambience and personal spiritual engagement. There is a partnership between internal and external sound and stillness. Nan Shepherd wrote that 'place and a mind may interpenetrate till the nature of both is altered' (Shepherd, p. 8). What sometimes occurs in a place that contains a quality of 'gathered stillness', profoundly suggests an experience that is hard to explain in terms of physical auditory characteristics alone.

Notes

1 Paul Horn (1969/72), CD: *Inside the Taj Mahal*. CBS Records: 11062-2.
2 Andy Stoller, interview with the author, quoted with permission.

References

Blesser, Barry and Salter, Linda-Ruth. *Spaces Speak, Are You Listening? Experiencing Aural Architecture*. Cambridge, MA: The MIT Press, 2007.

Bohlman, Philip V. 'Music Inside Out: Sounding Public Religion in a Post-Secular Europe', in Georgina Born, *Music, Sound and Space: Transformations of Public and Private Experience*. Cambridge: Cambridge University Press, 2013, pp. 205–23.

Bregman, Albert S. *Auditory Scene Analysis: The Perceptual Organisation of Sound*. Cambridge, MA: The MIT Press, 1994.

Clarke, Eric F. 'Music, Space and Subjectivity', in Georgina Born, *Music, Sound and Space: Transformations of Public and Private Experience*. Cambridge: Cambridge University Press, 2013, pp. 90–110.

Claudel, Paul. *The Eye Listens*. Port Washington, NY: Kennikat Press, 1950.

Cox, Trevor. *Sonic Wonderland: A Scientific Odyssey of Sound*. London: Vintage, 2015.

Golding, William. *The Spire*. London: Faber and Faber, 1964.

Hendrix, John Shannon. *Architecture as Cosmology: Lincoln Cathedral and English Gothic Architecture*. New York: Peter Lang, 2011.

Howard, Deborah and Moretti, Laura. *Sound and Space in Renaissance Venice*. New Haven, CT: Yale University Press, 2009.

Hussey, Dyneley. 'The Musician's Gramophone', *The Musical Times* 98 (London), 1957, p. 140.

Knight, David B. *Landscapes in Music: Space, Place and Time in the World's Great Music*. Lanham, MD: Rowman and Littlefield, 2006.

Murray Schafer, Raymond. *The Soundscape: Our Sonic Environment and the Tuning of the World*. Rochester, VT: Destiny Books, 1994.

Pallasmaa, Juhani. *The Eyes of the Skin: Architecture and the Senses*. Chichester: Wiley, 2012.

Pentcheva, Bissera V. *Hagia Sophia: Sound, Space and Spirit in Byzantium*. University Park, PA: Pennsylvania State University Press, 2017.

Reznikoff, Iegor. 'On Primitive Elements of Musical Meaning', *JMM – The Journal of Music and Meaning*, 3, Fall 2004/Winter 2005, Section 2. www.musicandmeaning.net/issues/showArticle.php?artID=3.2.

Shepherd, Nan. *The Living Mountain*. Edinburgh: Canongate Books Ltd, 2014.

Street, Seán. *The Sound Inside the Silence: Travels in the Sonic Imagination*. Singapore: Palgrave Macmillan, 2019.

Truax, Barry. *Acoustic Communication*. Norwood, NJ: Ablex Publishing Corporation, 1984.

Vitruvius. Trans. Morris Hicky Morgan. *The Ten Books on Architecture*. New York: Dover Editions, 2015.

5

WALKING THROUGH URBAN SOUND

In the Park

It is an irony that while urban environments made up of architectural spaces offer extraordinarily varied sonic opportunities for study, at the same time they provide almost infinite visual distractions to lure us away from active listening. In many locations within our towns and cities, sounds meld and blend into amorphous 'soups' of noise, which make it hard to extract the sometime subtle songs of some of the more reticent instruments within this complex orchestra. Yet these spaces, within daily reach and experience of millions of people, offer rich opportunities for the study of sound, if we but discipline our listening to separate the elements of the orchestration and critically analyse what it is that surrounds us. As Augoyard and Torgue remind us:

> Let us listen to our cities. Is it not the very nature of the urban environment to make us hear, whether we like it or not, this mixing of sounds? Dull murmurs, machine noise, the shifting and familiar acoustic racket created by people – every human moment has a sound signature, usually composed of many sounds together.
>
> *(Augoyard and Torgue, p. 4)*

In this chapter, I would like to 'drill' down into the mix of those 'many sounds together' in an attempt to isolate some of the component parts of urban sound; in order to do so, I intend initially to revisit recordings from a personal archive, balancing their witness against the filter of memory. In late April 1999, I visited Paris, staying at a small hotel close to the Pantheon in the Latin Quarter. On this occasion, I had decided to keep an audio diary based on various locations, using mini-discs, at the time a popular format. Twenty years later, I exhumed the recordings and listened again. (Fortunately, I retain some equipment that can still read this old technology.) One recording in particular caught my attention, because it somehow confirmed a sound memory that I had retained, and also because it offered a varied soundscape that seemed to typify how city sounds can change within a short compass.

It is a sound walk that began in the Luxembourg Gardens, and progressed as I moved out and across the boulevard Saint-Michel, into a Metro station, onto the platform and finally onto a train. The recording documents the various 'rooms' I entered and exited on this short journey – probably about fifteen minutes of recorded time. There is the crunch of gravel in the gardens as I walk, children in the play area, watching a puppet show, and the clip-clop of a small group as they pass me on pony rides. As I come to the park gates, the street ambience enters, gently at first, like a stream, and increasingly brutal as cars and buses jostle and accelerate. I must have stood for some time, waiting to cross. Clearly, judging from the sound, I am not moving; all the urban noise is going on around me. Now I am walking again, entering the station. Through the ticket barriers, down stairs and onto the platform. It is a big space, with echoes. Something changes, and I become aware of an approaching train. Ticking electrical relays as it approaches, and a growing rush of air, forced into the station ahead of the physical object. It enters. The sound feels immense, almost terrifying. Next, the doors open and I am in the compartment. A murmur of voices. It is quite full, standing room only. In the next compartment a busker is playing an accordion. After a minute or so, the recording ends.

This, briefly, is the chronology of the journey, but I realise as I listen, that this recording, unheard for all those years, unlocks visual memories through auditory signals that are amazingly familiar to me. Not only that, but associations come to mind that I am sure did not occur to me at the time, with all my senses at work on experiencing the moment and simply moving from one place to another. It feels as though I had heard it yesterday, and the sensory associations it stimulates are vivid. It dawns on me that I have held these sounds in my memory all this time, ready to replay them at any time. The rustle of leaves in the garden, the children's voices, the change through movement from 'room' to 'room', ending in the claustro-phobia of the Metro. The act of recording the walk has printed the moment onto two devices simultaneously: the machine and the mind, and for two decades it has been available to listen again. In fact, the sound memory has been much easier to access than the recorded audio. By making a conscious decision to preserve this series of moments from the last months of the twentieth century, the events of those fifteen minutes have continued to surround me as they did on that spring day. Time has become a crucial dimension in the exploration of this excursion, and it is appropriate that it should do so, since sound, as we have said, moves through time, just as we do ourselves. As Richard Koeck has written:

> If we look beyond the perceived interplay between the culture of vision and sound, and more closely at the temporal qualities of our built environment,

we can perhaps agree that the city is a temporal construct and, therefore, so is architecture. Physically, cities and buildings change and require mainten-ance, and their performance is evaluated over time. Philosophically, archi-tecture can be seen as a reflection of a particular time and its underlying values, ideologies and belief systems. Formally, we design and regard spaces and places in terms of the way rhythm is expressed architecturally.

(Koeck, p. 103)

When we are new to a place, we are listening and watching in surround-sound and with flood-lit illumination. Pauline Oliveros called it 'primary or initiatory listening' which 'gives us relationship to place and continues to unfold through one's lifetime' (Oliveros, p. 248). Familiarity breeds a dulling of perception as the brain selects and deselects from the live library of visual and audio events at the centre of which we constantly find ourselves. The art of attention is to sub-vert these filters, and to experience everything as if for the first time. As Oliveros says: 'Listen to everything all the time, and remind yourself when you are not listening' (ibid., p. 28). This makes me want to go back again to the recording, to tune in the details and reflect on the memories they evoke. At the same time, picking up on Koeck's point above, I must understand that my recording is now an historical document; the walk I took then, as chronicled on the disc, would sound – however subtly – different, were I to repeat the exercise today. Apart from weather conditions, urban changes in the interim, such as new buildings, freshly planted vegetation, alterations in vehicular transport, and the season of year, will prove that time has moved on, just as it always does, altering the world as it passes. Attempting to undertake a sound walk through almost any of our cities at the height of the Covid-19 pandemic would have been to create a sound document of a very different character. We build into our consciousness the idea of how a place *should* sound; to witness it without familiar auditory clues, or abnormally changed, can be a deeply disturbing and disorientating experience. To stroll along empty sidewalks, cross silent streets, to be confronted by shut shops and closed subway systems is a near apocalyptic scenario that many believed belonged only in science fiction movies, prior to 2020. Memory is constantly feeding our expectations, based on data accumulated through previous experience. We all retain something timeless in our memories of a place, so for a first-time visitor to an urban environ-ment emptied of its human populace, silent streets would be a definitive reality, a criterion by which future visits would be judged. The walkways through the Jardin du Luxembourg remain for me a touching place, connecting with both my own past in the city on my youthful walks in the 1960s, now a source of comparison with more recent explorations, and with the artistic and literary history of Paris itself. In *The Invention of Paris*, the writer and publisher Eric Hazan wrote:

Whether Jules Vallès, Léon Daudet, André Gide, Jules Romain, Jean-Paul Sartre, Michel Leiris or Jacques Roubaud, there is scarcely a Parisian novel or diary that does not feature the Luxembourg, central and symbolic as it is of a Left Bank that is seen as maternally welcoming students, writers, publishers and bookshops, art and experimental cinemas, avant-garde galleries and artists, not to mention the foreigners who arrived in the wake of Oscar Wilde, James Joyce, Joseph Roth and Henry Miller.

(Hazan, pp. 90–1)

The link between my time and all these people and the eras in which they lived and worked here, is the garden itself, notwithstanding the passage of time, and its shifts both scenically and sonically. My recording was taken in spring 1999, and at the other end of that century, the writer and theatre critic Paul Léautaud was among the many who walked these paths, and in his journal entry for 4 May 1901, he wrote:

> Dusk gave the whole garden an endless depth, and a light mist was floating. I was on the terrace not far from the greenhouses. In the lower part of the garden, the fountain rose and fell almost noiselessly. Soon the drum began to beat. They were about to close. I dreamed that I was facing a beautiful landscape of Baudelaire's....

(quoted in Hazan, p. 142)

The pond, where he heard the fountain, is close to where my recording starts. I understand what Léautaud means when he writes of the 'almost noiseless' play of the fountains' waters, a presence as much as an actual sound, and the idea of a drum-beat to signal the park's imminent closing is a marvellous one: I imagine a muffled funeral drum to mark the gentle silencing of the light, and the garden's return to its own solitude, its own ambience, without human intervention or occupancy.

Sometimes the significance of sound only strikes us in retrospect, and we realise how much we have heard without consciously articulating it to ourselves. We must also accept that no one sense supplies all the information we require to operate within the world. Listening to the early minutes of my Paris recording, I pay attention to the rustling of the leaves in the Luxembourg Gardens. Some sounds, taken on their own, can be ambiguous; wind in trees is a good example. By isolating a sense, we create a kind of abstraction, a detachment from reality at the very same time as a drilling into the moment. Is that the sound of leaves blowing in the breeze, or is it rushing water I can hear? Listening more intently, something gives it away, perhaps some perspective, or the context of other sounds around the trees, and the mental picture is restored. There is also personal experience and memory to aid me here; I *know* they are trees, because I was there, and I *saw* them. Were I more of a botanist, I would suffer no such confusion; a wood full of varied trees is a community, but it is a community of individuals. I am guilty of a gross generalisation. Trees are exemplars of how to be oneself and a member of society at the same time. If an attentive ear in the park on a sunny day needs help in identifying the specifics of the woodland, a gentle summer rain shower might help. Rain is silent until it touches a surface, and in forestry, as David Haskell expressed so elegantly, 'the rain's sound refutes any attempt to use a single idea to isolate the tree from its community. Every falling water drop is a tap against leafy drum-skins. Botanical diversity is sonified, calling out under the drummer's beat. Every species has its rain sound, revealing the varied physicality of leaves' (Haskell, 2017, p. 6). Thomas Hardy, at the very start of his novel *Under the Greenwood Tree*, listens to the language of the woods:

> To dwellers in a wood almost every species of tree has its voice as well as its feature. At the passing of the breeze the fir-trees sob and moan no less distinctly than they rock; the holly whistles as it battles with itself; the ash hisses amid its quiverings; the beech rustles while its flat boughs rise and fall. And winter, which modifies the note of such trees as shed their leaves, does not destroy its individuality.
>
> *(Hardy, p. 7)*

Sound and memory are indivisible, and certain situations inevitably trigger references in the mind, as the senses suggest parallels and other impressions. For instance, at this moment, it is a comfort to know that the voices of certain trees – some more than others – can mislead even the most knowledgeable country person:

> And wind-enamoured aspen – mark the leaves
> Turn up their silver lining to the sun,
> And list! the brustling noise, that oft deceives,
> And makes the sheep-boy run:
> The sound so mimics fast-approaching showers,
> He thinks the rain begun,
> And hastes to sheltering bowers.
> *(Clare, from 'Summer Images',*
> *in ed. Tibble, vol. II, p. 10)*

In the word 'brustling', as so often John Clare finds exactly the right verb to describe the agitation of leaves in the wind. His sonic observation is equally faultless, and in the poem, the country lad is fooled, for all his familiarity, into believing in a change in the weather. Edward Thomas writes of sound rooms with as much precision as almost any poet, and trees haunt his work; indeed, his very first poem 'Up in the Wind', written in 1914, describes the complaint of an inn-worker from Kennington in south London, cast up in a remote pub high above his home, surrounded by a beech wood.

> … it makes a noise
> when the wind blows, as if a train was running

The other side, a train that never stops
Or ends. And the linen crackles on the line
Like a woodfire rising.

(Thomas, p. 5)

There is the ambiguity of perception, fuelled by the experience of an urban consciousness, interpreting a rural environment. Thomas's childhood home had been in south London, so he understood the shift in perception. He would also have identified with an outsider's perspective; the voice of trees can focus and accentuate human isolation through their whispering. On the other hand, while recording in Greenwich Park, also in south London, in 2019, the BBC radio producer Julian May found a tree that, instead of making sound, seemed to actually swallow it:

> It was a programme about the susurrations of trees, the different voices of them – the aspen for instance seems even have a tremulous name that mimics its sound. I ended up in Greenwich Park, with my microphone inside a yew tree. The thing about that is that a yew seems to be more about the absorbing of sound than creating it; we were surrounded by city sounds, planes, people in the park, ambulances going by, children playing and so on. I could hear all this from within the tree with extraordinary clarity without the sound of the wind. I realised that a yew tree is rather like a *Rycote* microphone windshield, I felt as though *I* was the microphone, and that the end of my programme about the sound of wind in trees, was actually a tree ingesting sound.[1]

The illusion was that May and the tree were for a brief moment, listening together, actively, intensely, to a world, the sound of which had been filtered of all distractions; he was a sonic observer in a kind of aural *camera obscura*. The hollows within the trunk of a yew are like an ear. The art of really hearing is to listen below the layers of the sonic world, become audio archaeologists digging for the tiny fragments of sound that either the cacophony of life obscures, or that we have become too desensitised to notice. Clare's exhortation to observation is part of what James Wood, a staff writer for *The New York Times*, calls 'serious noticing'. Wood reminds us that while many of us may not occupy ourselves very long with looking at things, writers do: 'it is what literature has in common with painting, drawing, photography' (Wood, p. 61). He quotes the great philosopher of looking and seeing, John Berger: 'A drawing of a tree shows, not a tree, but a tree being looked at' (Berger, in Wood, p. 61). By intense seeing (as opposed to looking) as with active listening, we search down to the core of things. We may apply it to any field of consciousness; in fact, for a naturalist such an application is a vital requisite – as Clare does – and into our daily urban lives. We should in particular consciously practise it in new situations, as we turn a corner, open the door on a new day, or enter a room of any kind. In terms of listening, we need to tune the transmission channels between our ears and our brain and consciously articulate to ourselves as we do so, 'now I am attending to the world'. The explorer Erling Kagge identified the moment of changed perception in his book *Silence*. Walking alone in the Antarctic, he noticed how

> the uniform whiteness was transformed into countless shades of white. A tinge of blue surfaced on the snow, somewhat reddish, greenish and slightly pink. The landscape seemed to be changing along the route; but I was wrong. My surroundings remained constant; I was the one who changed.
>
> *(Kagge, pp. 2–3)*

It is important to allow time and space for internal adjustments, and to acknowledge them when they occur.

Returning to the recording, I listen to the children in the distance through the trees. I listen harder: I can now detect different voices through tones rather than words. The little voices are like points of light, of various brightness, colour and intensity, sometimes separate and often coming together, coalescing into an amorphous mass of sonic delight as the puppet master works magic in their particular room in the park, just out of my sight, but close enough. A park is one of our outdoor places to be most consciously made up of rooms, an expansion of a domestic garden, which is itself a room, and sounds move through it from space to space, as though coming to us from the other side of a green wall. Amidst the galaxy of little lights, a mother may detect the spark of their own child's identity across the park's solar system. To me, they are as delightful as children's voices always are, but because they are not speaking my native language, their chatter has the abstract quality of pure music. Nearer to me as I walk, occasionally the ponies pass with their tiny human charges intent and slightly fearful on their backs. The predominant sound is the gentle hollow percussion of hooves as they encounter the park's gravel path, a sound that somehow conveys the weight of the animal, transmitting it onto the ground through the leisurely impact. The children remain silent, absorbed in the moment. This is something they will remember.

The soundscape moves on; a park is almost like a house without a roof. Somewhere, in another part, there is a place of great concentration surrounding outdoor chess games. There is a gazebo, with musicians giving a free concert. Bandstands in public spaces used to be a ubiquitous and much-loved institution, particularly in the UK: a music room within the wider room of the park itself. The therapeutic value of both requires no argument. In 1999, the cellist Yo-Yo Ma created, with the landscape designer Julie-Moir Messervy, a two-acre Music Garden in close proximity to the high-rise structures of Toronto's downtown offices and apartments on the shore of Lake Ontario. The garden was inspired by images evoked from Bach's *Six Suites for Unaccompanied Cello* and in particular the *Suite No. 1*. Thus there are six distinct 'rooms' corresponding to the six 'rooms' (movements) in the work itself: 'Prelude' evokes a flowing river, 'Allemande' has a spiral path through birch trees, 'Courante' has a butterfly garden and a maypole, suggesting the dance of the movement, 'Sarabande' has a tall conifer and a small stage for poetry readings and musical performances, 'Menuett' contains a circular pavilion for music and dance, and finally 'Gigue' has an amphitheatre with a stone stage, a further place for performances. Like all parks, it is completely democratic in its intention. David Knight has pointed out that 'it was designed and built expressly to reveal music in landscape, [it] is a remarkable urban feature and an ever-changing soundscape. As such, it is a place for therapy' (Knight, p. 188). This Toronto garden dramatises and accentuates the role of music rooms within parks in many parts of the world, where the sound of live performance blends with the ongoing music of the urban environment, complementing, softening and civilising the sounds of the city.

> The Toronto Music Garden can be therapeutic for someone troubled by stress or overwhelmed by sounds of the surrounding city. The combination of the place and the music being performed on an ad hoc basis can be meaningful for many visitors.

Sounds heard in such places can also overturn prejudices, surprising as they do the innocent ear with new experiences. 'To appreciate fully whatever the sounds are around us – or simply to enjoy silence, if that is what is "there" – we need to be open in order to listen and truly hear' (ibid.).

Now in Paris, I become aware of the park's choir in residence, the birds. They form their own texture: ubiquitous pigeons playing a base note, but beyond them the tones of a chamber orchestra, layers of sound spreading through the perspective of distance. There are the ubiquitous feral pigeons, vocal and close at hand; probably I was mostly aware of their presence at the time, and guilty of hearing but not listening to the other voices. Now I hear a song thrush, the two-note song of a chiffchaff, and the occasional small 'teacher-teacher' piping of a great tit. At one point, there is the stuttering of a black redstart. I notice that because to my English-based ears it is the least familiar amongst the chorus. The black redstart is quite a rare breeder in the United Kingdom, although it was found inhabiting London bombsites after World War II, and has since bred in Liverpool docks and even around the Sizewell nuclear plant. Mostly though, its presence and voice are an event to an amateur bird listener like me within the UK. On the continent of Europe, however, it is a common inhabitant.

My walk takes me out of the gardens at their most easterly gate, onto boulevard Saint-Michel, at la place Edmond-Rostand, where the boulevard intersects with la rue de Médicis. I might have left by a number of other ports. Had I chosen to do so, I might even have heard the sound of bees, for there are hives tended in one room of the garden, I'm told. So many characters within this green theatre. Eric Hazan's description is perfectly apposite:

> As a hall or a landing opens onto successive rooms to which it gives access, so the Luxembourg opens onto all the central quarters of the Left Bank. Near the school of apiculture it touches on Montparnasse; its main entrance is towards the Observatoire; on the side of the Orangerie and the monument to Delacroix it borders on Saint-Sulpice, and in this way communicates with Saint-Germain; only rue de Vaugirard separates it from the Odéon. And it is above all else, as Léon Daudet says, 'the respiratory centre, the vegetable lung, of the hard-working Latin Quarter'.
>
> *(Hazan, p. 91)*

Why Did the Sound Recordist Cross the Road?

When I reach the boulevard, a different kind of rushing sound, punctuated by particularities, overwhelms the park acoustic. At this distance in time, can I detect that this is the sound of a Parisian arterial road, a conduit into the city centre? Does it sound especially 'Parisian', or does it lack any real specific sonic identification marks? Memory helps me here; the occasional ancient 2CV was still on the road at the time, a sound familiar to my ears from my previous youthful sojourn in Paris in 1967. Motor scooters too, more than one would normally expect; this is the university area, and the Sorbonne is just across the street. I remember how in the 1960s we used to take our lives into our hands on our old scooter, dicing with the traffic along the Left Bank and down to what used to be ORTF – now Radio France – for freelance radio work.

Pallasmaa reminds us that cities sang differently in centuries gone by:

> Every city has an echo which depends on the pattern and scale of its streets and the prevailing architectural styles and materials. The echo of a Renaissance city differs from that of a Baroque city. But our cities have lost their echo altogether. The wide, open spaces of contemporary streets do not return sound.
>
> *(Pallasmaa, p. 55)*

Many urban environments have little to distinguish themselves these days until we come to detail, notably the use of car horns – some cities are 'found' symphonies of them – and then of course there is the music of language, the voices as they pass, either in conversation or these days engaged on phones. In traffic jams, Parisian motorists are often vocal in the expression of their frustration or irritation. Before motorised traffic, there was the noise of horses and carriages, more deafening and noisome than today, a different form of pollution to more recent times. City centres rang with bells, and those as much as anything spoke with the authentic voice of the room that was Paris, or Rome, or Florence, or Amsterdam.

As a child growing up in the north of England, I remember the sharp contrast in city sound between Sheffield, where my parents lived at the time, and Portsmouth on the south coast, where holidays with my grandparents were spent. Sheffield at the time still had its old tram system, and I loved them: the ship-like sway, and the clang of the warning bell; mostly, however, it was the grinding drone at corners that is a memory, as wheels and rails bit into one another. Like the noise of the cable cars in San Francisco, the tram sound of Sheffield will have defined the place sonically for a number of generations, and anyone who remembers them will be transported to a place and a time by simply listening to a recording.

By contrast, the public transport system in Portsmouth was equally fascinating, simply because it was so different. Here, the trams from before my childhood had been replaced by smooth trolley buses. These also took power from overhead cables, but unlike trams, they used no rails, but glided silently through the city on tyres. The trolley bus seemed – and to me, still seems – a wonderfully eco-friendly creation; running noiselessly along the streets, with no pollution, their only threat was perhaps to unwary pedestrians and cyclists who might not hear them coming. Inside, there was the low hum, rising slightly to a higher pitch as the vehicle accelerated, as if we were riding on a large milk float. It was to this child a comforting, rather sophisticated sound: a relief from all the confusing city noise outside. Just as a Londoner would recognise the sound of a London Routemaster bus when played a recording, I am certain that I would know a Portsmouth trolley bus if I heard it again. A city possesses many rooms, but each city is its *own* distinctive sonic room.

Boulevard Saint-Michel jolts me back to my Paris recording. Another 2CV splutters past, and an angry Parisian shouts at a jaywalker who failed to wait for the crossing light. What else tells me where I am? My recording is in stereo, so my headphones provide me with evidence of traffic approaching from the left as I wait my turn to cross, then it shifts as I reach a pedestrian island in the centre. In pure sound terms it does indeed feel like an island in the midst of a choking sea of pouring combustion engines. One day perhaps this sound may itself become completely consigned to history. In the meantime, my ears tell me from the recording that the immediate concern is self-preservation, and the focus needs to be primarily on the visual, with the auditory playing its supporting role in terms of the perception of distance, proximity and safety. There will be time to remember and analyse later. This does not mean that I am not affected; urban stress may be subdued, but it remains capable of affecting us at a deep level. Salomé Voegelin has written:

> As I walk through a busy urban street I try to ignore the incessant hum of thick traffic, the noisy commotion… around me. However the fact that I do

not listen... consciously or willingly does not mean that these sounds do
not shape the reality as it presents itself to me.

(Voegelin, p. 11)

In fact, to the engaged ear, it can be a key part of the personality of the place.
The sound of the car horn provides in particular a strong sense of local identity. In
Paris, it is an extension of the human voice in expressing a view on the perceived
incompetence of others, or impatience with a lack of movement. Michael Stocker
has pointed to a comparison in usage of car horns between Egyptian and US cities
as an example of how much a part of the communal voice of a place such relatively modern devices have become, illustrating a continuity in cities such as Cairo
that simply does not exist on Western roads.

> The roads in Egypt are unlike the tracks of destination found in the west;
> they are rather like paved "tendencies" strewn with potholes and the detritus
> of opportunistic use. As roads they are used for all manner of traffic, simul-
> taneously displaying a 6,000 year history of transportation – from walking
> and goat herding to pack camels and donkey carts – all intermingled with
> motorised vehicles of all stripes. The cars and trucks are not expressions of
> personality here; rather they are more like motorised beasts of burden.
>
> *(Stocker, p. 48)*

This, Stocker suggests, places the sounds of the modern Egyptian city within an
historical context, beyond the individual personalities and egos of those inhabiting
it; the expression here is what it has always been: a part of a community.

> Drivers weave towards their destination using the car horn as a courtesy
> signal, notifying slower traffic of a rear approach with a delicate "tap, tap" on
> the horn. This tapping is so habitual that even in cases where there is little
> risk of collision, the "tap, tap" is still expressed, sort of like a "tipping of the
> hat" to other drivers. Hundreds, or even thousands of these horn taps calling
> across the city soundscape does thicken the noise field considerably, but it is
> not the angry sound of car horns heard in the States, rather it is the sound
> of courtesy – altogether a different thing.
>
> *(Ibid.)*

It is also evidence of an important fact that must inform this journey through the
spaces of the world: a city is a room in the international house, and as we decorate
our personal spaces to reflect who we are, the attentive ear, informed with some
prior knowledge, has the capacity for identifying our place at any one time; being
able to 'read' a place sonically enables a growing understanding of the similarities
and differences between us, things to be embraced and valued. 'This [in turn] all
points to a more fundamental characteristic of our species; that creating acoustical

territories may be among the first expressions of human will – second only to the will to emerge from the womb' (ibid.).

Memory is triggered by all sorts of prompts, and it only takes a tiny audio clue to unlock a scene and a situation, as any good audio drama producer will tell you. The traffic continues around me, the cumulative effect of a composite engine made up of *many* engines pulsing and roaring at different pitches, tones and volumes, just as did, in their own way, the small sparkles of children's voices and the fragile frequencies of birds in the park. Once upon a time, many composers gained inspiration from birdsong – from folk song to Haydn to Respighi to Olivier Messiaen, not to mention those who came before and after them. The rhythms of the internal combustion engine and the train changed the sound of life fundamentally; so was born the music of that room in time called the twentieth century: jazz, blues, and rock & roll. Like it or not, now as in the past, most of us live in a noisy place, and the sonic implications are both subliminal and profound, sounding in our ears and vibrating through our bodies from street level. The composer, musician and sound artist Nathaniel Mann has made some interesting observations on this aspect of listening:

> Recently I've been enjoying a new set of very effective noise-cancelling headphones, which have surprised me in the ways they can actually enable me to hear more! A good example was at a busy train station where major building work was taking place; between the hustle, the throb of diesel engines, roar of generators, the sound was overpowering. I turned on the headphones and to my ears the bulk of the noise was eliminated, but immediately my feet and legs started listening – or at least my listening priority shifted from ears to limbs… I was aware of a pneumatic drill shuddering through the entire platform. This wasn't the first time I'd been struck by the importance of embodied listening. Whilst working with indigenous Brazilian singer Akari Wauja to record his traditional singing, it became quickly apparent that much of the raw force of his music was transmitted by his rhythmic stomp, travelling through the red earth and up into my own legs. In order to convey this to listeners I buried a hydrophone directly beneath his feet during the recording sessions to capture the powerful thud.[2]

We deceive ourselves if we believe that listening belongs only to the ears, and this aspect of awareness becomes crucially important when we consider the sounds that surround us. Tramping horses from the past on the boulevard Saint-Michel would have once shaken the very ground, while now we experience a subtler but no less pervasive vibration on this same road on a busy day. Now I am across to the other side. The traffic is behind me, and there is pavement noise. Shop fronts and side streets leading back into history, and in particular to the ancient and venerable buildings of the Sorbonne. I remember Georges Perec and Gaston Bachelard, both of whom had strong associations with the Sorbonne. Perec, one of my inspirations for writing this very book, studied history and sociology here, and Bachelard, as part of an illustrious academic career, was the inaugural chair in History and Philosophy of the Sciences at the Sorbonne from 1940 to 1954. His books of lyrical and poetic philosophy have informed me for years, and I pause with the idea that he might perhaps have once crossed here, walking over to the Luxembourg Gardens, gathering inspiration and material for his chapter 'Nests' in *The Poetics of Space*. Certainly, finding a bird's nest in his own garden started him thinking about the nature of domestic space:

> A nest, like any other image of rest and quiet, is immediately associated with the image of a simple house… A nest house is never young… Not only do we *come back to it*, but we dream of coming back to it, the way a bird comes back to its nest…

(Bachelard's italics). Bachelard reminds himself of a touching poem by Jean Caubière, 'The Warm Nest':

> The warm, calm nest
> In which a bird sings
>
> Recalls the songs, the charms,
> The pure threshold
> Of my old home.
> *(in Bachelard, pp. 118–20)*

Pavement Art

The sound of another room. Here on the sidewalk I have entered a different environment with a distinct set of conventions. Brandon LaBelle has likened the way we adjust ourselves to this space, to the movements of a dance. Certainly, having navigated the rushing traffic, with its directional rules and rhythms of stopping, starting, acceleration and turning, the pedestrian joins a continuing random pattern of interrelation between bodies. 'Pivot, shift, and then release, the stepping body learns the promise of the horizon from the perspective of the sidewalk: this line of pavement, of stone or concrete, acts as a blank page for the imagination' (LaBelle, p. 123). The recorder reflects instantly the human community I have just joined; without the aid of the visual, and coming to this audio narrative as a newcomer, I might find myself bewildered by this babble of voices and footsteps on the move:

> Free passage [in this space] is… a continual side-stepping to avoid bumping into others, creating or modulating the gait of the walker by adding a step

there or a hop here to the rhythms of being free. Private and public, the sidewalk is a zone for sharing all the small details of what it means to be, to move, and thus, to interact with or against a context.

(Ibid., p. 124)

To complicate the sound picture, the trajectory of my journey is across the sidewalk towards the entrance of the train station. I am not joining the lateral journeys of the existing occupants of the sidewalk, but passing through their room, and the sonic effect is one of disorientation. Without visual references, it is confusing, but then memory supplies a context, and a mental picture returns. I regain a sense of myself as an individual within a community, albeit fleetingly, both an observer and a participant in the improvised choreography of the pedestrian community. 'The mediating space of the sidewalk… delivers an acoustical thrust found in a soundscape that might be heard as a superimposition of all that comes flooding from *without* and all that surfaces from *within*' (ibid., LaBelle's italics). Snatches of conversation, approaching and departing footsteps, sound from all directions. The pedestrian can participate or not, entering into an awareness of his or her surroundings, or create a conscious separation, say by engaging in a private conversation on a phone, or deliberately shutting out their environment by listening through headphones to another sonic world of music or speech. (Such devices were less in evidence back in 1999, but they were present nonetheless.) We may engage with public spaces by experiencing them, or exclude ourselves consciously, creating an auditory disconnect between the mental and physical place where we are in bodily terms, and the imaginary or cognitive invisible rooms of the mind. In truth, we have always done this, even before the arrival of the mobile communications devices to which we have now become so attached. Walking engages us in actual and/or subliminal participation in an environment. Part of us may be mentally lost in contemplation of an inner idea, while another part is committing the act of being in the material world, to experience and memory, and yet another is preoccupied with the practical business of getting us from A to B. That is precisely why these auditory clues remain so potent, even after twenty intervening years.

The sound artist Colin Black is highly experienced in the 'reading' of Place, and for him, the selection of the location itself if a key part of the artistic process. Rather than impose layers of interpretation onto soundscapes, or create overtly documentary interpretations and explanations, Black frequently prefers to allow only the subtle aesthetics of the place itself to guide the process, as with his 2012 work *Soundprints: The Prague Pressings*, in which he followed his instinct, inspired by the immediate surroundings, 'to subconsciously guide me with the goal of experiencing and recording new and authentic sonic events and environments' (Black, 3.1.3.).[3] The piece thus largely aims 'to form an aural psychogeographic map of my movement, non-chronologically, from one location to another through the urban soundscape of Prague'. Black remained constant in his determination to allow the place to dictate the audio agenda, arguing that

> this psychogeographical approach allowed me to be sensitive to locations in a way in which I could not have been if I was simply 'hunting for sounds'. Applying this approach also allowed me to collect location recordings without first judging their validity for inclusion in the work, and as a consequence it opened up creative options that would not have been available otherwise.
>
> *(Ibid.)*

The sound walk, be it in Prague or Paris, places the location in the foreground, rather than simply 'wildtrack' or a background sound effect; it allows the place its voice, valid in its own right, without justification. The field recording thus may be viewed (or rather heard) as the purest example of unmitigated witness, an example of honest, pure listening without judgement. It is indeed a most potent carrier of memory:

> *Soundprints: The Prague Pressings* is… a sonic vestige, a mnemonic, an overlay of "mythology" and human imagination being projected onto the sonic geographical locales melding with and possibly replacing the lived experience of the listener… As we listen in closer to the modulating abstract and non-abstract soundscape of the work, the aim is to reach a point where memories are not projected onto the sonic locations, but somehow they seem to entwine with the locations. In this sense the work challenges the listener to ponder if these memory sites are somehow energised by the past or if they are a projection from the frame of humanity in the present?
>
> *(Ibid.)*

Time passes between the moment of recording and the reliving of that moment through the recording; the sound walk moves through time and place, and sitting in an office in a distant city now, I hear myself cross a Parisian sidewalk as it was that day, at right angles to the flow, left and right, of the prevailing human tide. 'From street noise that washes over the sidewalk to shouts that break from windows, the sidewalk soundscape is a medley' (LaBelle, p. 124). LaBelle articulates my recording so precisely, it is as though he has been listening with me. Replaying it now, I wonder how I endured this assault of chaotic, conflicting sounds. I remind myself that my brain was operating multiple filters of sight, smell and temperature readings, as well as making decisions and choices about where to go next, considering if I needed to purchase a train ticket, whether I had to change trains at some point on the journey, and so on. As Voegelin also reminds me:

> Sound renders the crowd massive and persuasive, becoming ever denser and more intimidating, encroaching on my physical space. Their stomping

feet reverberate off the hard and shiny architecture… They are everywhere, coming closer and closer, engulfing me in their physical presence.

Switch off the drone of hammering footsteps and the aural hubbub of human activity, the crowd shrinks immediately, the frightful beast is tamed. Now all I see are people bumbling along, minding their own businesses, nothing to do with me.

(Voegelin, p. 11)

Like Voegelin, I can 'switch off' part of my reception equipment to make it all more bearable, but to imagine, as Eisenberg suggests, 'space imbued with absolute, undifferentiated silence… soundless space… is as otherworldly as non-spatial sound… Within the realms of human experience and the social… sound is constitutive of space, just as space is constitutive of sound' (Eisenberg, in Novak and Sakakeeny, p. 194). Many neurological and indeed physical conditions are affected by sound, whether through in excess or deficiency.

On the urban street, numerous storefronts seek to lure us in, and almost as many cafés, bars and restaurants also beckon. Were the pedestrian to succumb to their enticements, they would immediate find themself within a particular space, each in a way unique, and yet as often as not, smoothed to sonic sameness by the homogeneity of piped music: 'mood music' or 'elevator music', often given the misnomer of the brand we know as *Muzak*. By whatever name it is identified, there is little escape. Joseph Lanza underlines its ubiquity:

As restaurants, elevators, malls, supermarkets, office complexes, airports, lobbies, hotels, and theme parks proliferate, the background, mood, or easy-listening music needed to fill these spaces becomes more and more a staple in our social diet. Indeed, background music is almost everywhere…. Quaint piano recitals comfort us as we wait in bank lines, telephone techno-tunes keep us complacently on hold, brunch Baroque refines our dining pleasure, and even synthesized "nature" sounds further blur the boundary between our high-tech Platonic caves and "real life."

(Lanza, p. 2)

Casting an eye quickly along the line of retail temples on the boulevard, I remember imagining their internal soundscapes, and considering whether or not I should go inside to confirm the idea on the disc. Judging by the evidence of my recording, I clearly decided against it, preferring to take my chances underground.

Into the Underworld

My simple walk thus far would have presented problems to someone who was severely agoraphobic. Now I am entering another world, abruptly moving into a space operating through a totally different set of sonic rules, where all the rooms are tunnels, and all sound is contained, echoing, reverberating and swirling, an alien place in which we comfort ourselves through habit and regular routine, but in which we are all strangers. Here space closes around me, threatening claustrophobia and hallucinations of a different kind, bred by limiting what I see and accentuating what I hear. The mysteries of subterranean sound will come back to haunt us again in a later chapter. We civilise our public tunnels by tiling them, papering their walls with advertisements, sometimes playing music in them, but for the most part, we do not linger, unless it is to ponder our direction. The London Underground, the New York Subway, the Paris Metro and the troglodyte rail systems in other great cities around the world: they are inhabited by transient beings as a utility, moving from one place to another as quickly as possible because they must, shutting out the idea of the sheer weight of the city over them, and the close proximity of their fellow travellers by closing the door of their personal room, protecting themselves with a book or a paper or a headset. These are places where most often the dominant sounds are hurrying feet, the distant low screech of the trains, and inside them, often, a space that closes around us. We do not dwell on what lies heavy over us; this is no walk in the park, although as we rush through the subterranean darkness, the gardens of the city spread their roots over us, reaching down, the dead sleep in their graveyards around us and the stone of our edifices threaten to crush us. No wonder an underground carriage is so often a relatively quiet place. Some deep inner feelings are common to all travellers, no matter upon which system they travel. Of the London Underground, Peter Ackroyd wrote: 'It is not really a place at all. It is a process of movement and expectation' (Ackroyd, p. 138). Our shining walls disguise the primeval, so I do not think of myself as being buried or lost. But what if all the lights suddenly went out? Then I would be left with only sound, darkness, and time itself would take on a new form. Ackroyd evokes another paranoia: 'What if there is no sound? What then? A silent station is a disquieting and even a cursed place' (ibid, p. 143). I am, for this moment, a cave-dweller; without the lights and the wall tiles, with their names identifying a particular station, I would grope through earth and rock, with no compass, and the sound would change too. I am in a strange city, suddenly doubly strange, because if everything failed, nationality would count for little here. 'Deep time' is what Robert Macfarlane calls the chronology of the subterranean in his book *Underland*:

> Deep time is the dizzying expanses of Earth history that stretch away from the present moment. Deep time is measured in units that humble the human instant: epochs and aeons, instead of minutes and years… Deep time opens into the future as well as the past.
>
> *(Macfarlane, p. 15)*

We have tiled over the earth and the clay and the rock around us, but it is there nonetheless, and the smooth walls of the Metro throw our sound back at us, surrounding us with anonymous presences in strange rooms that, once we have all gone home, may continue to echo and resonate their eerie interconnecting ambience into their own space. In allowing these thoughts, how far I have come in a few yards from the bright, air of the park, its thrushes and chiffchaffs, and the leafy whispers of the chestnut trees they inhabit. Was it really only five or so minutes ago, as the timer on my playback suggests? This is subterranean thinking. Listening to my twenty-year-old recording again, the tunnel part of the sonic journey is more of a pure distillation than the sounds that came before, because, in a sense, down here sound has nowhere to go. Reaching the platform, the audio offers me a new perspective: slightly drier, more intimate. I hear my own footsteps stop. A pause. I imagine myself examining the destination board, noting that this is the RER B line, which would take me to the Stade de France if I so desired. The relative quiet on the platform tells me that a train must have just left the station. I can hear that there are just a few other people around, but gradually the space fills up with other presences, and there are quiet conversations close by. I notice the sound of an American couple chatting, unfamiliar vocal tropes in a murmur of prevailing French. Then there is a slight blast of air on the microphone; although I cannot yet hear the train itself, that gust is enough to tell us that one is approaching. The recorder reminds me of the sound of circuits ticking along the line, another clue to the imminent arrival, and the dynamic of movement. On the platform that day, I will have felt a sudden brush of air across my face. Mostly, because we have been robbed of so many daylight visual references, sound is everything in the antediluvian world; 'the echo flourished, raging up and down like a nerve in the faculty of hearing…' (Forster, p. 200) writes E.M. Forster in *A Passage to India* and so it is in these caves, for disguise them as we might, our underground systems are a series of caves; through these conduits human beings flow in common with power, data, water and sewage. These tubes give all sound a new character, an alternative sonic reality in which I become like a corpuscle circulating through the bloodstream of the city. That pulse of air I felt just now from the approaching train is a typical moment in the subterranean life, where every sound and change of temperature is noted; the gust of air is noteworthy because it is so alien down here. I listen again: even my microphone has noted it. This is where we must travel, through this network separated from darkness and pure sound only by the artificial generation of electric light.

> The underground… is a space of creaks and murmurs, a slow shifting of acoustical particles that hover on the threshold of perception, and which carry the possibility of threat, danger and inversion, suggesting that what lies underneath surreptitiously mirrors what lies about in full view.
>
> *(LaBelle, p. 5)*

The train bursts into the station, an acoustical shock to the widened space of air and light that awaits it; brakes scream, catches are released and doors slide back with a smooth roar and a clunk. The occupants of the platform transfer themselves into the rail cars, and we are closed into a new room, already fully occupied, but somehow, with various forms of physical compromise, seemingly almost always capable of receiving more bodies. I have exchanged the liquid sound of tunnels for the claustrophobic dry matt of a box. Of the Paris Metro, Marc Augé has written:

> The law of the metro inscribes the individual itinerary into the comfort of collective morality, and in that way it is exemplary of what might be called the ritual paradox: it is always lived individually and subjectively; only individual itineraries give it a reality, and yet it is eminently social, the same for everyone, conferring on each person this minimum of collective identity through which a community is defined.
>
> *(Augé, p. 30)*

As with every house – if we can stretch a point to call this labyrinth of disparate sound worlds within a world, a 'house' – there are many rooms in which the unwary traveller, not familiar with the rules of navigation, might become mired and lost. There are, on the other hand, those habitués, the regular travellers, who through long custom and routine are able to 'read' the sonic signals coming from around the next bend. They are able to interpret the score of the subway, its dynamics, crescendos and diminuendos, in a way not given to the rest of us, and they 'can be recognised in the perfect mastery of his or her movements. In the corridor leading to the platform, the traveller walks swiftly but without rushing; without letting on, all senses are on alert' (ibid., p. 7). These gifted ones, owners of the secret sonic code of the subterranean rail system, be it in Paris, London, New York or St Petersburg, are guided by the sound, rather than confused by it:

> When, as if surging off the walls lined with enamel tiles, the noise of an oncoming train becomes audible, disrupting most of the occasional riders, this traveller knows whether or not to hurry, either by assessing the distance to the boarding area and taking a chance or not, or by having identified the source of the crescendo of din and heard in this lure (peculiar to stations where several lines intersect and which for this reason French calls *correspondances*...) a call from beyond, the deceptive echo of another train...
>
> *(Ibid.)*

It is significant that Augé called his book *IN the Metro* (my capitals). These places are immersive in every sense, and this sonic journey through sound rooms and sub-rooms has been a study in audio immersion that preserves time in a way no set of photographs ever could. Having followed the silken thread of sound down here, out of the light and into the lair of an imaginary Minotaur, I cannot resist imagining the whole thing in reverse, coming out of audio darkness into the bursting sound of the pavement, the road, across and into the park, then relaxing back into the soothing balm of chestnut trees, birdsong and the distinctive sounds of children. Either way, the experience is almost hypnotic, so that when the recording ends, it is like emerging from a cinematic experience, and for a moment I find myself blinking, acclimatising myself to a different reality. All the while, my eyes and mind remained here in my studio, I was aware of my environment, and at the same time I was in another place and time. Holiday snaps would have provided isolated moments, but because sound is temporal, both as it occurs and as it is relived, this has been a real-time experience, moving step by step through places that do not change, except by gradually fading and cross-fading with one another as I proceed on my way. These rooms do not have doors as I leave them: they simply merge and blend, finally giving way to a new set of voices. There are memories of course that provide for me a context, something that others coming to these recordings would not have without some sort of 'programme note', but what most matters is that the sound room represented by those fifteen minutes on the sound stage, the interconnected chambers of a French city on an April day at the very end of the twentieth century, is here preserved as evidence of how it was then. It exists unadorned by explanation; is that a limitation? In some ways, perhaps it is, and yet on the other hand, would not a commentary dilute it, compromise it, turn it into simply background noise? In these recordings, from the walk in the park to the immersion of the sonic darkness of the Metro, the main event, the complete narrative, often has been the sound of the places themselves, unmitigated and uncompromised. Places have personalities; they also have walls, whether they are visible, physical or not. You can hear it in their voices.

Notes

1 Julian May, interview with the author. Reproduced with permission.
2 Nathaniel Mann, communication with the author, February 2020. Reproduced with permission.
3 Colin Black, *Radio Art: An Artist's Research and Practice, 2008–2012*. A portfolio of work created as a doctorial submission in the Sydney Conservatorium of Music at the University of Sydney. Thesis extract reprinted by kind permission of Dr Colin Black, courtesy of University of Sydney.

References

Ackroyd, Peter. *London Under.* London: Vintage, 2012.
Augé, Marc. *In the Metro.* Minneapolis, MN: University of Minnesota Press, 2002.
Augoyard, J.F. and Torgue, H. (eds). *Sonic Experience: A Guide to Everyday Sounds.* Toronto: McGill University Press, 2005.
Bachelard, Gaston. London: Penguin Books, 2014.
Eisenberg, Andrew J. 'Space', in David Novak and Matt Sakakeeny, *Keywords in Sound.* Durham, NC: Duke University Press, 2015, pp. 293–307.
Forster, E.M. *A Passage to India.* London: Penguin Books, 2005.

Hardy, Thomas. *Under the Greenwood Tree.* London: Penguin Classics, 2004.

Haskell, David George. *The Songs of Trees: Stories from Nature's Great Connectors.* New York: Viking, 2017.

Hazan, Eric. *The Invention of Paris: A History in Footsteps.* London: Verso, 2010.

Kagge, Erling. *Silence in the Age of Noise.* London: Penguin, 2017.

Knight, David B. *Landscape in Music: Space, Place and Time in the World's Great Music.* Lanham, MD: Rowman and Littlefield, 2006.

Koeck, Richard. *Cine-Scapes: Cinematic Spaces in Architecture and Cities.* New York: Routledge, 2013.

LaBelle, Brandon. *Acoustic Territories: Sound Culture and Everyday Life.* New York: Continuum, 2010.

Lanza, Joseph. *Elevator Music.* London: Quartet Books, 1995.

Macfarlane, Robert. *Underland: a Deep Time Journey.* London: Hamish Hamilton, 2019.

Pallasmaa, Juhani. *The Eyes of the Skin: Architecture and the Senses.* Chichester: Wiley, 2012.

Stocker, Michael. *Hear Where We Are: Sound, Ecology, and Sense of Place.* New York: Springer, 2013.

Tibble, J.W. (ed.) *The Poems of John Clare, Vols I & II.* London: J.M. Dent & Sons Ltd, 1935.

Thomas, Edward. *The Collected Poems of Edward Thomas.* London: Oxford University Press, 1981.

Voegelin, Salomé. *Listening to Noise and Silence.* New York: Continuum, 2010.

Wood, James. *Serious Noticing: Selected Essays.* London: Vintage, 2019.

6

LANDSCAPES, BEACHSCAPES, SOUNDSCAPES

Elemental Forces

I have a recording of a Japanese temple bell, given to me by the radio producer Julian May, collected just outside Kyoto. It lasts for 42 seconds, and I often come back to this sound because for me it makes a fundamental point about listening. A bell is struck to excite its resonance, and then it gradually fades to silence. Between those two poles, violence and silence, there lies a world of sound, a sonic spectrum in which we find ourselves listening closer, harder, more actively to the changes in the narrative of the sonic decay. When does the bell actually stop sounding? When we can no longer hear it? When its vibrations can no longer be measured technically? Perhaps. Yet to speak of sonic decay is misleading, because as the sound moves beyond our human capacity for hearing it, so other sounds become evident. We are listening to something made in an outdoor space, a room itself that is surrounding the gong-like sound of the temple bell, a sacred space bounded by trees. At first, the voice of the bell dominates. It commands our complete attention, then as it fades, our ears strive to follow its tone, the message in it, until, our hearing sense tuned and alerted by the effort of this interaction, we realise that what we hear next is something we had not been listening for: the sounds, faint and at varying distances, of birdsong, a gentle rustle of leaves, the ambience of woodland, sounds to which our attention has been drawn by focusing on the space left by resonance. We hear the fuller presence of the temple's sonic room, augmented subtly by the serial rooms around it, as though the event is happening inside another, which in turn exists within another and so on, rather like Matryoshka dolls. It is a sense of heightened awareness that the examination of stillness, silence and quiet sounds encourages. The poet Edward Thomas, sitting in a railway carriage at a train station in the English countryside one summer just before the start of World War I, caught just such a moment as this in his most famous poem:

> And for that minute a blackbird sang
> Close by, and round him, mistier,
> Farther and farther, all the birds
> Of Oxfordshire and Gloucestershire.
> *('Adlestrop', Thomas, p. 25)*

He hears sound over and *within* silence infiltrating his space through the window, and the close bird, drawing his attention beyond its song to all those other rooms coming to him unhindered by walls, transmitted by air and a still late June afternoon. I have the memory of my temple bell, the Japanese birds and the heat haze of Thomas's sunlit landscape in my mind as I open the back door of my suburban house and step into the garden. By this action I have shifted my personal mobile room, in the form of the body space it occupies, from the office, through the acoustic landscape of the family home, into my nearest outdoor room, enclosed on three sides by a five foot high fence, insulated with shrubs, bushes and flower beds, carpeted by a lawn and bounded by high beech trees. Merleau-Ponty wrote of the 'here' the body occupies at any one time: 'Bodily space can be distinguished by external space and envelope its parts instead of spreading them out, because it is the darkness needed in the theatre to show up the performance' (Merleau-Ponty, p. 115). This perfectly articulates the subjectivity and receptivity of the space I occupy as a listener moving through the rooms of the world, entering the illusion of unconfined outdoor space, fenced nature that was man-made in the creation of my garden, one of a long line, left and right of personal 'properties', that are 'rooms' bounded by walls but not by roofs. Beyond the trees at the bottom of the garden, there is a field. It is an ancient field, and local legend has it that some of Henry V's archers once used it as a practice area before the Battle of Agincourt. Accordingly, it has been named 'Archer's Field'. These days, we do not hear the sound of bow and arrow, but occasionally the thump of a football when the students from the local school come for sports days.

Today it is a winter's day, so there are no leaves on the beech trees. It is a Sunday, and the field is empty, apart from a solitary man with a dog, far across on the other side. Occasionally the dog barks, and the man throws a ball. On a still day I can hear, as did Edward Thomas, the sounds coming from far rooms, out of sight and obscured by houses and trees. On such days, my sonic horizon exceeds my visual limits by several miles. Not today; today there is a storm, and I have come to confront it, inspired by the sounds captured by Rob Bridgett's Newfoundland recording of external weather playing on internal sound spaces, discussed in Chapter 2. Today, I seek to find the source – or as near as possible – to the elements that knocked on his door, and beat on his windows and walls. By stepping outside, I feel my way into the matter of Place.

The first thing to notice is how the presence of rain and wind around me limits the audio horizon. I can hear nothing beyond my immediate surroundings, or at least, my senses are unable to separate the individual sounds that cumulatively amount to a cacophony. It is like being at a noisy party, surrounded by loud revellers, the sound of which obscures the voice of someone trying to attract my attention on the other side of the room. In the end, my eyes tell me they have resorted to sign language in order to communicate. I can see the trees on the far side of the field signing, pulled left and right by the storm, telling me that there are stronger-still gusts coming towards the house, but I cannot hear them, because the weather that already surrounds me is shouting too loudly. I record, using a strong wind muff on the microphone. I first concentrate on general ambience, captured in the centre of the garden, a 'room' of about 16 by 12 metres. Next, I move around the borders, picking out as far as I am able, the individual sounds of plants, sparse and skeletal at this time of year, apart from a few shrubs and bushes. Finally, under the giant beeches, I pause, as the rain pours down and the trees, so recently green then gold with leaves, now confess their naked branches, sounding the winter. On a whim, I place the microphone through a gate in the fence, into the field beyond, at arm's length, for a few moments. Then I walk slowly back to the house, while the rain lashes and the wind beats around me.

Back in the office, I download and play back the recording. There is the house door, closing behind me, and then the storm swoops in from all sides. A few drops of rain fall on the mic, although not a lot; the shield has done its work. I hear the close proximity of the plants, quite sheltered by the fence, their presence only betrayed by the patter of raindrops, in near focus. They are surprisingly unmoved by the gales. Under the beeches, it is a different story; the rain beats down, the branches roar in a way I had not noticed at the time. The real revelation, however, comes when I tentatively let the microphone go through the fence gate and into the open field. Whatever it actually hears of the storm is completely obliterated by the huge blast of wind noise. It is something my naked ears could not have demonstrated from the shelter of the garden, and it graphically illustrates how totally my personal space, sheltered by fences and a hedge, has the sonic properties of a discrete room. Out in the field, there is another sound space completely, a great hall of gale force wind that the uppermost branches of the beeches have been trying to communicate. How hard, almost impossible, it is to break down this storm into its constituent parts. All the wavelengths are broadcasting together. I see and hear what it is that our walls and double-glazed glass has been protecting us from all these years on nights like these, when the storms come in off the Irish Sea. My little suburban garden is so insignificant, given the great space full of the formless forces in the room next door, just the other side of the fence panels and the pyracantha bushes.

Each lateral layer that surrounds me in this weather obscures the sound beyond it. Birds may sing somewhere, the gantries at the container port will be clanking and grinding as usual, but it would take a big sound indeed to even compete with this maelstrom. A storm makes the sonic world of bodily space shrink, obscuring the wider show going on beyond it. Standing at the centre of the circle, in a room of air bounded by fences on three sides and our house on the fourth, with a road beyond it, on a still day there would be more to analyse, and the component parts of the soundscape would be easier to isolate. Yet even in the midst of the maelstrom it is clear that the idea of being in a space shaped by the elements alone is an illusion. It is extremely difficult to locate an environment that is unmitigated or in some way shaped by our presence in it. Without the houses, the shrubs, the garden compartments, the fences, the sound of this place would be quite different. Even the sound of the countryside was changed by successive enclosure acts in Britain between 1604 and 1914, turning open fields and common land into rooms bounded by hedgerows, transforming ecology as well as economy. Every time a new stone is placed in a wall, or a meadow is mown, there is sonic intervention. There is a singing in the telephone wires, and it is haunting, eerie and beautiful, but it is a sound that has been introduced to landscape, and it has been appropriated by the winds as they blow in from the sea, up the river and across the field. The thirty-four-year-old Henry David Thoreau, writing in his journal for 22 September 1851, noted it with a wonder approaching the metaphysical:

> Yesterday and today the stronger winds of autumn have begun to blow, and the telegraph harp has sounded loudly. I hear it especially in the Deep Cut this afternoon, the tone varying with the tension of different parts of the wire. The sound proceeds from near the posts, where the vibration is apparently more rapid. I put my ear to one of the posts, and it seemed to me as if every pore of the wood was filled with music, laboured with the strain, – as if every fibre was affected and being seasoned or tuned, rearranged according to a new and more harmonious law. Every swell and change or inflection of tone pervaded and seemed to proceed from the wood, the divine tree or wood, as if its very substance was transmuted. What a recipe for preserving wood, perchance, – to keep it from rotting,– to fill its pores with music!
>
> *(Thoreau, p. 81)*

Always the Same, but Never Again

Our presence in – and effect on – the spaces of landscape have become more damaging since Thoreau listened to the transmitted hum of the wind through the telegraph wires. While noise pollution has grown, many species have fallen silent, some animal voices have changed, and the very sound of a river's flow has in some ways altered. Climate change takes many forms, with many symptoms, and listening is an underused measure of what is happening around us. When we step into the open air, we are entering a room in which we are but co-tenants; we share the occupancy, and although our structures and habits have profound effect, the other residents have voices too. Changes in temperature, humidity and wind speed are all factors that help to determine how the world sounds, not only of itself, but in the effect it has on the sonics of animal communication. This, even before we consider the loss and destruction of habitats; who else would walk into a neighbour's home and wreck it? The world's sound is not what it was; the rise in tides, and the increased frequency of floods, cyclones and hurricanes and other extreme weather conditions will destroy old soundscapes and create new patterns of acoustics.

Thoreau was writing before mass communication, and the double-edged sword that was to come with the ubiquity of electronically transmitted sound. Likewise, the English polymath Charles Babbage, born in 1791. Babbage was a mathematician, philosopher, inventor and mechanical engineer who originated the concept of the digital programmable computer. His words, taken from *The Ninth Bridgewater Treatise: a Fragment* of 1837, may be read today on a number of levels, not least relating to radio waves, the internet, and even as a metaphor for collective conscience:

> The air itself is one vast library, on whose pages are forever written all that man has ever said or woman whispered. There, in their mutable but unerring characters, mixed with the earliest, as with the latest sighs of mortality, stand forever recorded, vows unredeemed, promises unfulfilled, perpetuating in the united movements of each particle, the testimony of man's changeful will.
>
> *(Babbage, p. 29)*

Rooms as we normally think of them can shelter us, protect, and to an extent separate one sound from another, enabling us to close the door on competing ambiences. Reading the sound of the interrelating spaces that constitute the environment is a gift, but also a skill to be learnt. As the weather changes, a fisherman can tell by the way the water slaps on the side of his boat, when it is time to head for home. We may sense the ambience contained in any space within a moment of entering it, standing at the edge of things; two adjacent rooms touch, and new horizons open – in some cases, quite literally. It is easy to stand and take in a great wide moorland vista, noting the contours, shadows and shifting cloud patterns of the view, forgetting that it is all a composite, a vast painting made up of sometimes minute sonic details. In May 2019, producer Julian May and composer/musician Tim Shaw made a programme for BBC Radio 3 called *The Water's Music*. The idea behind the work was actually to *collaborate* with a small section of landscape – in this instance, a Northumbrian burn – and out of that collaboration to create a composition. By moving rocks and logs, the sounds of the stream were adjusted, 'tuned', and a piece of music slowly emerged, as Shaw and May explored the sounds of the brook in intimate detail, from the tiny tinkling trickle near its source to its disappearance under a road. Recalling the process, May said:

> What we found was that there were several 'rooms' within this journey. There were parts where it seemed to go through a little tunnel, we could hardly get the microphone through. And then there'd be a little waterfall and a pool, and that would be like a small separate room and the acoustic changed. And beyond there would be the sound of the wider moor and things going on around.[1]

Thus producer and musician intervened in various ways, at one point building a ladder of rocks to create a chord as the water flowed down. They used hydrophones, recording underwater to capture the music of the burn from its bed. They also tied these hydrophones to pieces of wood, letting them drift downstream as 'sound pooh-sticks'. In a pool by the burn they recorded strange pings, the sounds of tiny aquatic creatures as they added their own song to the mix. Surfacing again, they stretched a rod across the burn with microphones attached at intervals along it. Recording first one, then another they created stepping-stones – in sound. What emerged was a piece in three movements for Northumbrian burn, rocks, logs and aquatic beasts, composed from three small interconnected rooms, a physical moment playing its own song within the huge continuing symphony of landscape. Most poignant of all, it is a record of human and place interacting creatively, as the little stream continued on its way. As May reminds us, 'the fascination of flowing water is that it is always the same… but never again'.

Tidal Rooms

Walking to the beach of Llandanwg in Gwynedd, North Wales, the ear is shielded from the sound of the sea until the last moment by a high range of sand dunes at the end of a narrow lane. It is an ideal place for a case study on this particular quest, because the beach and its immediate hinterland, by accidents of terrain, form distinct sonic rooms. The approach is quite domesticated: a community of houses and bungalows, a narrow bridge over a railway line, a caravan park, a small café and beach shop, a car park with a public toilet. To one side, seemingly almost buried in the dunes and facing inland across marshy fields to the sheep-filled hills beyond, is the ancient chapel of St Tanwg's, known for good reason as 'the church in the sand', dating back to the thirteenth century. Between the fields and the hills, there is a main road, but most of the traffic bypasses this corner, heading north and south to Porthmadog or Barmouth. As a child, the writer Philip Pullman lived and went to school in this part of West Wales, and came to know the terrain in intimate detail. For any visitor, it is interesting to compare an image of the road down to the sea with his, as described in his 1990 novel, *The Broken Bridge* through the eyes of the central character, a teenage girl called Ginny:

> Inland, a range of great grass-covered hills, not quite mountains but as high as hills could get, rolled endlessly away out of sight; but on this side,

the seaward side, there was a space of magic and beauty… It was a mile wide: all the land between the main road and the sea. There was a grassy field below the road, then the lane with her house, then more fields, then a railway line, then another field and the sand dunes and the beach. To the right there was a parking area and a little shop, and the tiny caravan park that you couldn't see from the house; and to the left there was the estuary, where a little river, which only a few miles back in the hills was tumbling swiftly among rocks, spread itself out wide and slow through a tidal lagoon. Beyond that there were more dunes and, at the very edge of the horizon, an airfield from which tiny silver planes occasionally took off, to skim over the sea and vanish.

(Pullman, pp. 12–13)

While he was at school here, Pullman's stepfather worked for the RAF at the field at nearby Llanbedr. Today, the military have gone, but tiny silver planes still skim out and over Llandanwg. For the boy that was Philip Pullman, this landscape was immensely important and formative; he knew it intimately, and he bequeathed it to his main character in the book:

She owned it because she'd drawn it, from the insects on the dry-stone walls to the decaying church half-buried in the dunes to the little bridge that carried the railway line over the estuary. And she owned it, finally, because she loved it

(ibid., p. 13)

To be here physically, is to provide the one element Pullman left to the imagination, and this is the sonic presence of the place. It is one sound room after another, and the degrees of auditory information seem to be infinite, varying almost from one footstep to another. The car park, with the café on the right-hand side, the dunes straight ahead, and open fields to the left and behind, is almost literally a room, walled on three sides. When there is no vehicle activity, it is remarkably quiet, but this is a place of relative values; inside the church lies an auditory experience of a distinctly different character. It is hard to believe, sitting in the tiny church, that it is only about 20 metres from the high-water mark of St George's Channel, south-west of the mouth of the River Artro, where it enters the sea. It is more than silence or stillness: it is the ambience of intense concentration, accrued over centuries. My recorder is not even registering a sound, apart from the occasional creak from the rafters. Across the tiny church is a giant wooden beam, which gives the visual illusion of lowering the ceiling, creating the effect of a tunnel peopled by the ancient pews. It is a place full of ancient atmosphere. The scarf of the sand dunes wraps itself around the weathered stone, guarding it from the sea; once, so the church guide tells me, the sand itself broke in and overwhelmed the tiny interior, but now it feels to be a place of cloistered insulation. Even outside, the sound of the beach is only a murmur, except on the stormiest days.

Walk through the narrow pathway between those dunes, however, and things change. Crossing the car park, there is still little hint of that other sound world; then turn a corner, and pass through the narrow sunken path between the high banks of sand, where the sea becomes visible. Now my recorder wakes up, as the sea wash sound comes pouring up towards me, until I reach the beach, where the roar, rush and tug of the tides give me their full widescreen stereo picture. On a windy day, the thunder of the water on Llandanwg Beach swamps the senses: it is full of a mixture of sand, stone and pebbles, a range of stones that make most walks a combination of careful stepping and stumbling. Just at the point where I am standing listening, the beach shifts its character. To the right, it is all rocks, smooth, grey, some with strange patterns of erosion. To the left, particularly at low tide, it is a smooth expanse of peerless sand following the curve of the bay. This is a sea that is seldom quiet, and it interacts with the beach in its own personal way, a conversation that to a local ear could only be this particular place. Looking straight out to sea, all might seem familiar, a typical marine view: the waves are variegated grey and blue, broken or smoothly rolling in. It is when the material substances of water and land touch, that the discussion begins in earnest. Just to the north there is a headland, and on the other side of that the vast sand beach of Harlech, itself bounded by the rolling dune banks of Morfa Harlech, and beyond that the mountains of Snowdonia, with Porthmadog and Portmeirion nestling at their feet. That beach has quite a different sound to where I am standing now; to walk to it round the bend in the coastal terrain would take perhaps ten minutes. Yet if ever there was a clear articulation of individual voices in a landscape, this is it.

These are rooms with all portals open, and just as we change a space by our presence in it, so unseen forces alter the sound of a shoreline as they pour in through the windows of air, brushing, touching, striking and shaping its character. Other elements are more predictable, such as the ebb and flow of tides, but they all interact with wherever the waves make landfall, according to the fabric of the place. On Crosby Beach, Antony Gormley's iron men stare out silently from his landscape art work *Another Place* as they are enveloped across the wide shallow beach. For those who know, the sea sends signals, high frequency, moving in with a subtle hiss, before the ground starts to glisten, and then drowns. At Old Leigh in Essex, the wading birds know first; soon the stranded fishing boats will be afloat again. Listening to the work of sound recordists on the different coasts of just one island is enough to reinforce the understanding that every corner on the map has its own sound, according to its relationship with the elements on a particular day, at a particular time, dependent on the moon, the winds, weather fronts and temperature. In July 2007, Phil Riddett captured the shingle beach of Birling Gap in East Sussex, the sound of millions of tiny stones shifting as the water broke over them, then sucked them back out, gradually changing the point of contact between land and sea. The very fact that this sound is held on a commercial recording featuring twelve shorelines around the British Isles is enough to show the diversity of spaces where one surface or surfaces comes up against others. On the east coast, Richard Margoschis caught a calm sea on Wells Beach, Norfolk; it is a recording that through pure sound alone takes this particular writer to another place entirely. In a childhood memory, I am on a small beach at Hill Head on the Solent, looking across to the Isle of Wight on an early summer morning, the water a perfect blue under the sky, and the child absorbing the moment, and the smell of ozone in the air. Contrast this with Simon Elliott's recording of a heavy sea on the rocks of Bamburgh in Northumberland on an early autumn day in 1997, where the roar is almost continuous, covering the senses in a wash of white noise, or Whitesand Bay in Cornwall after a winter storm a year earlier, preserved by Paul Duck, all compiled from British Library recordings and produced by Cheryl Tipp in the Natural History Recordings department (Tipp, CD, tracks 1, 8, 10 and 12). No one can ever claim to have listened to the sea on a shoreline in any definitive form, only a single place and time, and within the consequences of natural circumstances, particular to time and location. Every beach has its own set of voices, be it roaring water on rock, lapping currents in calm inlets, or even singing sands, as at Basin Head Provincial Park on Prince Edward Island in eastern Canada's Maritime Provinces.

To learn the language, temperament and moods of a beach, it is necessary to live through a cycle of seasons within earshot of one. During the 1920s, the writer Henry Beston built himself a two-room wooden hut that he called 'The Fo'castle' on the Great Beach of Cape Cod, a fragment of land more than thirty miles from the inner shores of Massachusetts. He published recollections of his time alone there in 1928 in a book called *The Outermost House*. Beston's work contains some of the most powerful evocations of the sound of the sea on shorelines ever written:

> It is a mistake to talk of the monotone of ocean, or of the monotonous nature of its sound. The sea has many voices. Listen to the surf, really lend it your ears, and you will hear in it a world of sounds: hollow boomings and heavy roarings, great watery tumblings and tramplings, long hissing seethes, sharp, rifle-shot reports, splashes, whispers, the grinding undertone of stones, and sometimes vocal sounds that might be the half-heard talk of people in the sea.
>
> *(Beston, p. 40)*

Through the long habit of listening, Beston came to understand the language and dialect of his neighbour, and learned to read how each phase of tidal conditions, every shift of the weather, and every turn of the wind played a part in the subtle modulations within the sea's continuously varied singing:

> Surf of the ebb, for instance, is one music, surf of the flood another, the change in the two musics being most clearly marked during the first hour

of a rising tide. With the renewal of the tidal energy, the sound of the surf grows louder, the fury of battle returns to it as it turns again on the land, and beat and sound change with the renewal of the war.

(Ibid., p. 41)

Beston's writing is in the company of a select band of natural world observers – Richard Jefferies, Richard Mabey, Tim Dee, Robert Macfarlane, Nan Shepherd and a few others – who blend knowledge with poetry in their writing. In such writers, indeed, the word 'observer' becomes something of a misnomer, because the best of such work places them – and their reader – at one with the place and its time, to the extent that there is a mutual understanding of how everywhere on earth is made of a series of moments; the given gift, or learnt skill, is to be able to interpret the key changes, when the music shifts to a new key. To live in, or adjacent to, any terrain, be it bucolic, urban, isolated or within a community, is to grow familiar with the soundscape, and to understand when a change is either to be expected and taken for granted, or to be noted and acted upon. Listen to where you are, but also keep an ear alert to what is happening outside your door:

> Late one September night, as I sat reading, the very father of all waves must have flung himself down before the house, for the quiet of the night was suddenly overturned by a gigantic, tumbling crash and an earthquake rumbling; the beach trembled beneath the avalanche, the dune shook, and my house so shook in its dune that the flame of a lamp quivered and pictures jarred on the wall.
>
> *(Ibid., p. 40)*

Henry Beston only stayed for a year from 1926–27, leaving 'in the year of the great tide' as he called it (ibid., p. x). As a sound recordist often plays back his audio away from its location, so Beston was only able to write his reflections in another place. While there, he was too close, never out of earshot of the prevailing sound, and it was only through memory that he gained the ability to truly hear and experience it objectively. In his writing, as Philip Hoare suggests in his introduction to Beston's masterpiece, he 'becomes part of the beach, the sea, the dunes, watching them as they change through the seasons... He is feral, nocturnal, tidal, tugged by the moon and the stars... The sea-sounds augur and echo the seasons' (ibid., pp. xx–xxi). Henry Beston's home – all that was left of it – was declared a National Literary Landmark of the USA in 1964. It was destroyed by a huge winter storm in 1978, ten years after its creator died.

Beston's experience chimes with the memory of a storm during the winter of 1988 that hit the east coast of England, evoked in the journal of the film-maker Derek Jarman. Jarman lived in a wooden beach house called Prospect Cottage, within sight of Dungeness nuclear power station. In the years up to his death in 1994, he developed and tended a garden on the shingle beach, a postmodern and context-sensitive place that even today forms an oasis in an eerie landscape where the detritus of the Cold War decays amidst tide and weather-shifting circumstances. Remembering that great storm a year later, he was drawn back to a childhood memory of the twister sequence at the start of *The Wizard of Oz*, in which Dorothy's home is spun and lifted skywards:

> The hurricane grew. A deep and continuous roar now underpinned the higher notes of gutter and drainpipe: the shrieks and groans and banshee whistling took on symphonic proportion. My Prospect Cottage never seemed so dear, beaten like a drum in the rushing wind that assaulted it and flew on howling after another prey. Down the coast whole roofs of tiles were lifted high in the air, to descend in a ceramic hail. A garden wall collapsed in a series of curves like a serpent, an ancient macrocarpa shredded like matchsticks. Outhouses groaned and slid off their foundations.
>
> *(Jarman, p. 19)*

Jarman first hears the homogenised roaring chaos of the storm, and then breaks it down into its constituent parts, its grammar and vocabulary. The room in his tiny cottage, and the space outside, become metaphors for his centre of perception as the storm seems to envelope the space like a Kansas twister. In 2019, the composer and sound artist, Sebastiane Hegarty visited Dungeness, a long self-promised journey in belated response to a letter received from Derek Jarman in July 1991. Hegarty has a fascination for bleak, haunted open landscapes, borderlands between worlds. His Dungeness project, which he called *Fog Signal Transmission* was

> one of a series of covert residencies and transmissions, which began in 2017 with a stay at Marconi's Lizard Wireless Telegraphy Station, site of the first 'over the horizon' transmission. The text [of *Fog Signal Transmission*] as subsequently included in a blog, was part of a 'performed' paper at the John Hansard Gallery (Southampton). The talk was followed by a live variation of the transmission of *Fog Signal* – called *Séance for six radios*.[2]

Dungeness, which Hegarty refers to as 'exquisitely bleak', is on the borderlands of worlds in more ways than one; closer to Calais than London, it is a place that seems to be forever straining to hear faint signals out of silence. There are relics of its frontier watches, abandoned listening and signalling posts. 'On the shingle, the derelict shell of a wooden shed is thought to have been built by Marconi as part of his experiments with the transmission of wireless radio signals across the English Channel.'[3] There is evidence too of other sonic experiments; when the feet stop moving across the shingle, the place becomes strangely still, in spite of its location, a shifting spit confronting incoming winds from the east. It has a reputation for silence, and this has over history, brought many listeners. At Denge – Greatstone – there are three concrete acoustic mirrors, part of the Hythe Acoustical Research Station, constructed by the Air Ministry in the 1920s, an early warning system designed to survey the air, with stations along the coast from Denge to Hythe, on to Dover and the South Foreland Lighthouse. These giant 'ears' listened for the propulsion of incoming enemy aircraft, potential premonitions of invasion that by the 1930s were rendered redundant by the invention of RADAR. Hegarty tested one of them, overlooking a military firing range:

> As I ascend the hill and reach the mirror, I hold a microphone out into the oracle (Auricle) of its hollow, and I am suddenly confronted with a burst of gunfire, the echo of its acoustic shrapnel shattering the mirror's derelict silence.

It is the ghost of a sound that has just occurred, a memory caught a moment after its sonic presence manifested itself through the air from a nearby firing range. 'Just as the mythical Echo wasted away and turned to stone, so too the percussion of the ballistics recurs, an echoic and fugitive spirit, mineralised in the concrete of the mirror' (ibid.). Beaches are places where incoming voices break through walls, sometimes carried towards us by winds, sometimes denied to us as the air changes. Jarman wrote of the sound mirrors as

> The Listening Wall… [that] could hear a whisper over the horizon – or the shouts and curses of Dunkirk, the drone of enemy bombers in Normandy… Here, lost in the shingle, reflected in the lake, beside this great monument falling into ruin, you can lament the heroes if you wish. Perhaps this is its finest hour, alone with nothing particular to listen to.
>
> *(Jarman, p. 72)*

Places such as Dungeness are rooms where we cannot resist putting our ear against the invisible metaphorical wall to listen. Lying in his bedroom, fitful and restless, Jarman noted how 'the rain wept through the night, quietened the grumbling shingle, stilled me into sleep. In the distance, the sea roared, churning the ochrous sandbanks' (ibid., p. 50).

Sebastiane Hegarty's Dungeness project has been included in his presentations, and has a context within a larger work, *Tapping the Air*, 'a highly choreographed re-animation of the project using field-recordings, imagery, text, voice and live micro-FM transmission.'[4] Hegarty both listens to and interacts with landscapes, particularly wild places where the elements transmit themselves and where human-kind has listened and sent messages into the air: 'At *Fog Signal* I decided to not only listen *into* the landscape, but also *introduce* other sounds into it' (Hegarty, blog, *Fog Signal Transmission*). Key among these sounds was an improvised Aeolian Harp, 'a cheap second-hand auto harp, "prepared" with the flotsam of wood, screw and polystyrene washed up onto the Ness'. Thus, although a human hand has introduced a musical instrument to the landscape, it is the wind blowing across that terrain that 'performs' the music itself. Dusk comes, and the ghostly duet begins, as the robotic beam of the Dungeness lighthouse automatically announces night fall:

> A line of pebbles cast onto the shingle traces an arc of auditory space and presence. The auto harp sounds, divining the air and revealing a concert of signals already present. I transmit to an unknown and unknowing audience, the transmission, like sound itself, disappearing in the moment of its appearance. Signals lost are sent, received and lost again. No one is listening, nothing is heard.
>
> *(Ibid.)*

Hegarty's work is haunting in a number of ways, and echoes the writings of the Norwegian artist, conceptual poet and composer Cecilie Bjørgås Jordheim, working with the translation between visual and auditive systems, concrete poetry and the concept of isomorphia. Through installations, visual scores and concrete poetry, Jordheim's work springs from an interdisciplinary agenda: between genres, fields of art and media, with the thesis that all visuals have sound. Composers have long sought to turn landscapes into auditory forms through music, sometimes reflecting the visual, at others directly seeking to create a sonic version. These include such orchestral pieces as Vaughan Williams' tone poem *In the Fen Country*, and Richard Strauss's *Alpine Symphony*, attempts to catch the mood and experience of landscape, either through abstract music or programmatic sound narrative, and transfer it to another room, in the form of a concert hall, recording studio or elsewhere. Jordheim has also interpreted a mountain in her piece *From the West Fjord* in the form of Stetind, the highest point of the Norwegian mountain range of Steigen, in the northern part of the country. Of this project she has written:

> Transforming a mountain into sound is about transforming something constant and solid into something ephemeral and linear. It is about compressing something eternal into a short interval of time. The act of conserving Stetind and its surrounding mountains through sound can be considered as a systemisation equal to drawings, paintings, maps, topography, and archaeological and geological research.
>
> *(Jordheim, p. 79)*

While it is true that such work 'fixes' an experience and turns the visual into sound, Hegarty's projects inhabit the place itself, and catch it at a moment when the rain fell with a certain force and direction, a particular wind blew across the terrain, and the air spoke in its own transient way. A place becomes a performance space in such circumstances.

The Movement of Air

Replaying a sound in a recording, even years after the event, can be a potent experience, because the memory of a sound carries with it a whole raft of circumstances that existed at the time of recording. One Christmas Eve, I was staying with my family on a hill farm in West Wales, bordering the Snowdon mountain range, not far from Llandanwg. As the day waned, I went out into the garden with my recorder, and looked down across a wide valley, towards distant hills covered in fir trees, punctuated by the occasional white stone cottage. There were sheep that seemed almost to glow in the dusk, and the landscape faded gradually towards darkness. I placed the microphone on a gatepost, and listened. A mountain stream murmured somewhere out of sight, just in front of me. A rook called, a solitary car wove up the lane to the right and then was gone. Apart from these sounds, it seemed the essence of stillness. The occasional voice of a single sheep created a sound event in the quiet that surrounded them, and that quiet 'amplified' as I looked and listened. A dog barked. Then there was only the stream. It wasn't silent by any means; it was a landscape represented sonically by its own continuing ambience, punctuated by small sonic incidents. It was that particular time between day and night that the French call *entre chien et loup*, the time of day when one cannot see the difference between a dog and a wolf. I watched the sheep, glowing white against the coming darkness. I heard the dog far across the valley bark again.

Listening now, far away from the moment in terms of time and place, is an act that conjures a vivid mental image of what I saw at the time. I can 'see' the white cottages, far away over the valley on the distant hillside, I can see my own cottage behind me, and beyond it a farmyard. I can even bring back to mind the glimmering sea that shone when all else had faded, away to my right beyond broken barns and naked trees. I can 'feel' the chill, and picture life going on in the cottage, where my granddaughter was excitedly looking forward to Christmas Day, everyone was playing family games, and the Christmas tree shone by the wood fire. Heightening this memory is the sound the recorder heard of which I was not aware, the movement of air across the microphone, the sense of the place printing itself onto the memory card. It is unmitigated, authentic and outside of intervention. It seems to be such a simple record of a moment, and yet it ignites memory.

The movement of auditory information through outdoor air is complex. It may begin as something fragile, even tiny, but its importance may far outweigh its audibility. A dog barking in the night is very different to that same dog barking on a sunny day. We may also consider the sounds we do not hear, as well as those we do; these small but significant signals may be at the mercy of a gust of wind. A key incident may occur the moment after I switch off, as soon as my microphone's back is turned; it is also highly likely that my recorder will not be able to pick out the subtlest nuances of sound, swirling through the landscape. Charles D. Ross wrote of how random shifts in climate, even the most minute, can reveal or conceal sounds across a landscape in the same way that light and shadow can manifest physical objects:

> Our air swirls in invisible whirlpools, streams up and down in reaction to temperature differences, and may vary considerably in moisture content from spot to spot. When the day is blustery or rainy it may seem a miracle that we hear anything at a distance.
>
> *(Ross, p. 7)*

Frequencies, intervening foliage, the undulations of land, water: there are many reasons why the sound of a landscape room possesses its particular character. Certainly my memory may be of a peaceful, quiet hilltop view across a broad vista operating its own slow visual fade, but listening again now, I realise that it was anything but silent, and further, while the world of sight may have disappeared into the dark, the sound of its presence continued unchanged, as it had done through immeasurable time, as it will be continuing now, this moment, far away from where I write these words.

Landscapes are full of sound, but they also possess mysterious acoustic shadows, pockets where audible signals seem to almost soak into the ground and vanish. Just as a concert hall is designed with sound as well as sightlines in mind, possessing its own character, likewise a terrain, whether man-manipulated or completely natural, contains its own idiosyncrasies. These may include spaces that appear to trap sound, or even apparently swallow it. There are examples of a perplexed observer of an event in a landscape noting that where there *should* be sound, the ear is defeated. During the American Civil War there were noted examples of acoustic shadows of this type across a number of terrains, that actually disrupted strategic decisions. At the Battle of Gaines Mill, for example, near Richmond, Virginia, on 27 June 1862, George W. Randolph, the Confederate Secretary of War, and a member of his staff Robert Kean were observing the action from a hillside at a distance of about a mile and a half. Kean later recalled the event in a letter to the British scientist John Tyndall, who later quoted it in his book on sound:

> Looking across the valley I saw a good deal of the battle... My line of vision was nearly in line with the lines of battle... I distinctly saw the musket-fire of both lines, the smoke, individual discharges, the flash of the guns. I saw batteries of artillery on both sides come into action and fire rapidly... Yet looking for nearly two hours, from about 5 to 7p.m. on a midsummer afternoon, at a battle in which at least 50,000 men were actually engaged, and doubtless at least 100 pieces of field-artillery, through an

atmosphere optically as limpid as possible, *not a single sound of the battle* was audible to General Randolph and myself. I remarked it to him at the time as astonishing.

(Tyndall, p. 306)

Tyndall would have been sympathetic to Kean's account; in his researches into sound in air, he had come across other examples of so-called 'silent battles' in history. Sheer volume of noise seemed to be a consideration; sound so great that the force of it through the air drove it beyond close witnesses, and manifesting itself, one might almost say, 'materialising' many miles away. Thus observers at the scene heard nothing, while people many miles away found themselves listening to carnage they could not see. Kean, in his letter to Tyndall, also noted characteristics within the intervening landscape at Gaines Mill:

> Between me and the battle was the deep broad valley of the Chickahominy, partly a swamp shaded from the declining sun by the hills and forest in the west (my side). Part of the valley on each side of the swamp was cleared; some in cultivation, some not. Here were conditions capable of providing several belts of air, varying in the amount of watery vapour (and probably in temperature) arranged like laminae at right angles to the acoustic waves as they came from the battle-field to me.
>
> *(Ibid.)*

Exploring the phenomenon in his book, Charles Ross identifies three possible combining factors: 'absorption by foliage or a large land mass, upward refraction due to temperature differences in the air, [and] upward refraction due to wind shear' (Ross, p. 35). Such climatic vagaries affecting the transmission of sound in a pre-electronic age could have far-reaching effects: 'Civil War commanders relied heavily on their sense of hearing in their planning and conduct of battle' (ibid., p. 43). Battles are often fought on broad lines of terrain, and in a world before radio, when those conducting the conflict could not communicate directly with their colleagues elsewhere on the front, the human ear was a crucial means of understanding the progress of hostilities within the landscape. In an upwind position, it would be difficult to hear sounds, say four miles distant if, for example, there was a strong adverse wind blowing at the time.

These are graphic and extreme examples of airborne sound over the earth. We do not need to witness a battle to observe the movement of sonic signals. On my Welsh hilltop, as dusk came on, a single sheep far across the fields embedded itself in memory, and I hear it, the frequency of the note reaching me as an event through the general ambience of the terrain across time. In the first chapter of this book, I remembered opening the car door onto this same hilltop, and experiencing the flood of the presence of the place as it poured in, pressing from all sides, rather like emerging from a box into an amphitheatre. This sensation can be experienced anywhere, even outside one's own house on a suburban street. Simply opening a door or a window in a house is enough to sense the relative widescreen perspective of the presence of the world outside. In a series of location-based radio programmes made about the seventeenth-century poet Henry Vaughan with Michael Symmons Roberts for the BBC some years ago, we explored the comparison between sonic spaces. Beginning with the box-like studio acoustic in which the announcer introduced the feature, Michael as producer then opened each programme with several seconds of recorded location sound, that poured in before the first words were spoken. It was broad stereo, and the mental auditory picture provided an eloquent image of the wide valleys of the Brecon Beacons in Wales, where Vaughan lived. It demonstrated the intention right from the start, that these were to be programmes rooted in the place itself, and that the location was to be throughout, a character within them, playing a major role in the narrative. It was pictorial, cinematic and it powerfully exploited the contrast between the enclosed sonic space of the continuity studio and the recorded witness of Vaughan's world. The landscape required no words to establish itself to the listener, explaining and describing its existence through the air, and on the air.

Notes

1 Julian May, interview with the author. Reproduced with permission.
2 Sebastiane Hegarty, correspondence with the author, quoted with permission.
3 Sebastiane Hegarty, part of a presentation at the John Hansard Gallery (Southampton) on 5 December 2019, included in the blog *Fog Signal Transmission*. Quoted with the author's permission.
4 Sebastiane Hegarty, personal communication.

References

Babbage, Charles. Ed. Martin Campbell-Kelly. *The Ninth Bridgewater Treatise: A Fragment. The Works of Charles Babbage, Volume 9.* New York: New York University Press, 1989.
Beston, Henry. *The Outermost House: a Year of Life on the Great Beach of Cape Cod.* London: Pushkin Press, 2019 [1928].
Jarman, Derek. *Modern Nature: The Journals of Derek Jarman, 1989–1990.* London: Vintage, 2018.
Jordheim, Cecilie Bjørgås. 'All Visuals Have Sound: the Verbalisation of Geography and the Sound of Landscape', in Eric Magrane, Linda Russo, Sarah de Leeuw and Craig Santos Perez, *Geopoetics in Practice.* Abingdon and New York: Routledge, 2020.
Merleau-Ponty, Maurice. *Phenomenology of Perception.* London: Routledge, 2002.
Noyse, Alfred. 'The Dane Tree', in Seán Street, *Radio Waves: Poems Celebrating the Wireless.* London: Enitharmon Press, 2004.
Pullman, Philip. *The Broken Bridge.* London: Macmillan Children's Books, 2001.

Robinson, Tim. *Connemara: Listening to the Wind*. London: Penguin, 2007.

Ross, Charles D. *Civil War Acoustic Shadows*. Shippensburg, PA: White Mane Books, 2001.

Thomas, Edward. Ed. R. George Thomas. *The Collected Poems of Edward Thomas*. Oxford: Oxford University Press, 1981.

Thoreau, Henry David. *The Journal, 1837–1861*. New York: New York Review Books, 2009.

Tipp, Cheryl (ed.). *Waves: The Sounds of Britain's Shores*. London: British Library CD NSA CD 84, 2011.

Tyndall, John. *Sound*. New York: D. Appleton and Company, 1896.

7

INTERVIEWING SPACE

Sound Exhumed

Forty thousand years ago, men and women sheltered from weather and danger in caves, and perhaps the very first thing they noticed was how the sound of themselves changed, reverberating back in strange ways that they did not recognise. Caves were the first rooms. Moving deeper into the darkness, they had only their voices as sonar to navigate tunnels and passages, and they would have quickly learned that a changed sound meant an altered space. In Chapter 4, the work of the composer and musician Iegor Reznikoff, and in particular his interest in the sacred relationship between the seen and unseen, was cited. His projects involving cave acoustics is significant in relation to the concept of how space, decoration and sound interrelate. Archaeologists, placing themselves in the position of the first cave inhabitants, moving through the dark, using their voices to bounce signals off walls as navigation, encountered a curious phenomenon, as David Hendy highlighted: 'When these archaeologists felt the sound around them suddenly changing, they would turn on their torches. And at that precise point they would often see on the wall or ceiling a painting' (Hendy, p. 4). Coming as they do from such a distant time, and yet preserved not only in a visual image, but more poignantly in a shared sound, these connections take us to some fundamental truths about our relationship between human identity and special sound. Similar phenomena have been shown to occur in a number of locations, such as in the area around Col de Portel in the Pyrenees, and Arcy-sur-Cure in Burgundy, where at one point, 'just where the resonance is really striking, there's a ceiling densely packed with animals of all kinds, and on the floor, the delicate outline of a bird' (ibid., p. 5). It is a little like discovering old advertisements in an abandoned subway tunnel, but with the addition of linked sound as an interactive response.

To witness this correlation between sound and image emerging out of lost time is haunting in every sense of the word, as Iegor Reznikoff underlines:

> It is indeed a very strong experience to hear in almost complete darkness the cave answer to a sound produced just in front or just under a picture of an animal, a bison or a mammoth. Since both the body and the cave vibrate, we can speak of an earth or *mineral* meaning of sound, but also, because of the relationship with the pictures, of an *animal* meaning of sound: we are thus naturally introduced to very deep elements of sound meaning.
>
> *(Reznikoff, 2.1)*

The field of archaeoacoustics unlocks important meanings to subterranean spaces, and we see our own rooms, chambers and halls in new ways, reflected by a time scale we had perhaps not considered before. The Hypogeum of Hal Saflieni (underground cemetery) on a hill overlooking part of Valetta harbour, in the town of Paola, Malta, only revealed itself – and its sound – in 1902, having lain undiscovered, dark and silent for thousands of years. A vast burial complex, originally housing the remains of about 7,000 individuals, it was in use from 4,000 to 2,500 BC. The first wonder of the place was its discovery after so long, and the second, its extraordinary sonorities. As Linda Eneix explained, such spaces are gifts to be treasured by archaeologists of sound:

> Archaeoacoustics has to do with the space and places where they [ancient peoples] were using their music, and how the sound behaved inside those spaces. Unfortunately, it is rare to find one of those places the way our ancient ancestors knew them.
>
> *(Eneix, p. 18)*

It is for this reason that Hal Saflieni has prompted such intense acoustic research; in 2014, it was the subject of a conference in Malta, in which findings and comparisons were shared. Immediately it became clear that the sounds unlocked when the Hypogeum was opened, exhibited a curious, otherworldly quality. It was also evident that this sound was both partly natural and partly cultivated: 'It seems the Hal Saflieni builders not only recognised the environment was inclined to produce sound effects, but they exploited it, intentionally using architectural techniques to boost the "super-acoustics"' (ibid., p. 27). During testing, one archaeologist

> reported that he felt the sound crossing his body at high speed, leaving a sensation of relaxation. When it was repeated, the result was similar but even more relaxing, accompanied by the illusion that the sound was reflected from his body to the strange red ochre paintings on the wall.
>
> *(Ibid.)*

For Iegor Reznikoff, Hal Saflieni is a key link between the Palaeolithic painted caves of France and Romanesque chapels:

> That people sang laments or prayers in the Hypogeum is certain, for a) it is a universal practice in all oral traditions we know, b) at the same period, around 3,000 BC, we have the Sumerian or Egyptian inscriptions mentioning singing to the Invisible, particularly in relationship with death and second life, and finally c) the resonance is so strong in the Hypogeum already when simply speaking, that one is forced to use it and singing becomes natural.
>
> *(Reznikoff, in ibid., p. 28)*

It is therefore curious that these extraordinary qualities were not immediately apparent – or at least noted – when the site was first opened for study in 1908. It was William Griffiths, writing in the *National Geographic Magazine* in 1920, who confirmed that with respect to one small niche or alcove in particular, 'it was noticed only a few months ago that any word spoken into this place was magnified a hundred-fold and audible throughout the entire underground structure' (Griffiths, quoted by Stroud, p. 40). Various experiments have been carried out, with mixed results, in the Hypogeum, but as the archaeologist Katya Stroud, Senior Curator of Prehistoric Sites at Heritage Malta, has written, the sound of Hal Saflieni represents the product of human intervention to mimic already sophisticated internal spaces, within a subterranean environment:

> In the Hypogeum, chambers carved to represent megalithic interiors have their ceilings carved to imitate a built roof of corbelled masonry, with one course overhanging the one below... Above all... the rock-cut chambers of Hal Saflieni allow us to study a system of interconnected spaces very much as they were conceived and experienced by a Neolithic mind.
>
> *(Stroud, p. 40)*

One particular part of the complex, that niche noted by Griffiths in his *National Geographic Magazine* account, became known as the 'Oracular Chamber' and Stroud notes an account of its acoustic properties as described by Temi Zammit, who was curator of the site in 1925:

> A deep low note uttered or hummed in or near the small cave, or the oval niche, resounds and vibrates in the chamber in a most remarkable manner. The oracular sentences were probably uttered, in the oval cave, in a deep voice which, breaking the silence of the place, must have greatly impressed the anxious devotee out in the dark passage.
>
> *(Zammit, quoted by Stroud, p. 41)*

To make and hear sound is evidence that we are alive, and to hear walls speak back heightens our sense of mystery, and evoke the supernatural and the strange, offering apparent evidence of voices beyond our own. Today we can dramatise sound by electronic means, but in the first instance, all fundamental changes in sound originated from its reverberation against surfaces. Likewise, the sound of a room tells us how to respond, as we step from such hyper-acoustic environments as Hal Saflieni or Le Portel, back into our mundane, everyday world. At each step we take, our senses interview our surroundings, and we respond accordingly; it is part of human survival.

Sound Under Sound

Entering a room, I hear its ambience, the general character of the place. As discussed in Chapter 1, and demonstrated elsewhere in this book, by recording an experience, we may open ourselves to some chastening revelations, as sounds reveal themselves in ways of which we may have been previously unaware. Moving around an environment throws up new perspectives, as we interrogate the particularities of the location. The world reveals itself in its details, so by simply placing a recorder or an active microphone on a table and letting it listen, we are capturing only a fraction of the story. There are small voices murmuring all around us, in themselves sometimes almost imperceptible, and yet each playing a part in the composite being and character of the place itself. As we shift our perspective, new sounds come into focus, and then seem to dissolve and cross-fade, just as if we were walking across a space full of people, each in their own conversation. A snatch of a phrase here, an intriguing piece of gossip there, coming and going as we pass by and into a new room within a room. To acknowledge these elements of the orchestra is to hear these surroundings in new and exciting ways. It is curious that by consciously engaging with this process, I find I have heightened my own sonic awareness; because I am attempting to focus the attention of my recorder on specifics, I find myself hearing things of which I was unaware. Not only this, but the act of sonic focus has the effect of printing the moment on my mind, so that *I* become the recorder. Memory is a major medium of preservation, as shown in previous chapters, in the broken castle turret, the resonating cathedral, or a Parisian street. My recorder was there to preserve it, but my mind was recording too, and unless memory fails me, it can play the sounds back, and the place returns to my present. If the time comes when I lose this ability, I hope that the preserved sounds on the machine's memory card will help me. In the early days of recording technology, sound recordists and producers used the wonderful phrase 'bottled programmes' to denote the function of playback. I had always considered an analogy for my gathered sounds to be that of a library; now I think about it, I like this idea: a row of sounds in bottles, lined up along a shelf, ready to be opened, and their message from the past released again to the air, in all their detail and colour. It is an attractive thought to picture a room's atmosphere as being a base colour, with the sonic events within it as details colouring the air, sometimes blending and sometimes flashing with a vivid identity that draws the ear to something that changes the space in some way.

It can be a fascinating process of discovery, to record 'blind', without monitoring, and allow oneself to be surprised by things missed by the ear. On the other hand, there are times when it is essential to hear what the microphone hears at the same moment as the happening itself. It can be revelatory, because by doing so, focusing our attention through headphones, there is sometimes an overwhelming sense of immersion, a feeling of oneness with the environment that releases new layers of perception. It is different to the taking of a photograph; with a camera, I have sometimes found myself missing the moment in the very act of seeking to capture it. With sound, it is the opposite: a sense of being *in* the moment, rather than standing outside it as an observer. 'I grew to appreciate the company of people who listen to the world…', wrote the poet Kathleen Jamie, observing two wildlife sound recordists, Tim Dee and Martin Leitner at work on location in her book *Findings.* 'They were alert to bird-cries, waves sucking on rocks, a rope frittering on a mast. Sometimes I'd notice them catch each other's eye, give a complicit smile, and I'd wonder what I'd missed' (Jamie, p. 54). While there are devices with the potential to submerge our consciousness in virtual reality, conversely the potential of a 'live' recording process that actually asks a place specific questions of its meaning, is to create *hyper-reality.* This can, of course, be taken further, when the work is developed in the studio; just as a photographer may wish to heighten a sense of drama by adding contrast, exposure, or brightness, post-production has the capacity of drawing attention to detail, and in effect saying to the listener, 'hear that?' This takes us into the realms of programme and sound art making, the enhancement or manipulation of sound for narrative or compositional purposes, but such story telling always begins with its raw materials. Above all, it starts with a desire to ask questions; just as an interviewer of people must care about them, and want to hear what they say, so a listener to a place must have an obsession with every sound, constantly tuned, as a painter or photographer takes in the subtlest variations of light. Earlier, we considered the work of Tim Shaw and Julian May, 'interviewing' a Northumbrian burn, interrogating the stream in terms of its process as it flowed across moorland. Out of this came a clear sense of the subdivision of place, breaking down what might seem to a casual passer-by to be general sound, into specific and significant voices, communicating a narrative and a music that grew out of a three-way collaboration.

Microphones, we should remind ourselves, do not have brains, so they need to be 'told' what to listen to. On the other hand, because they do not discriminate, as our senses do, they can teach us how to listen without prejudice. Once we hear as a recording device hears, it becomes possible to give value to the sounds that matter most. John Clare had the gift as much as any poet who ever lived:

> I hear rich music wheresoe'er I look,
> But heedless worldlings chide the brawling brook;
> And that small lark between me and the sky
> Breathes sweetest strains of morning's melody;
> Yet by the heedless crowd 'tis only heard
> As the small warbling of a common bird
> That o'er the plough teams hails the morning sun;
> They see no music from such magic won.
> (Clare, 'The Voice of Nature', in Tibble, II, p. 40)

It is in the next stanza that Clare writes what to me are the most meaningful and thought-provoking lines in the whole poem:

> Yet I see melody in nature's laws,
> Or do I dream? – still wonder bids me pause:
> I pause, and hear a voice that speaks aloud:
> 'Tis not on earth nor in the thundercloud;
> The many look for sound – 'tis silence speaks,
> And song like sunshine from her rapture breaks.
> I hear it in my bosom ever near;
> 'Tis in these winds, and they are everywhere.
> (Ibid.)

Sounding Great Village

Helen Tookey is a poet and a writer of creative non-fiction, based in the north-west of England; Martin Heslop is a sound artist, composer/musician and poet from Newcastle upon Tyne. Alongside their individual practices, they have been making work collaboratively for a number of years, work concerned with the ways in which sound and text interact, built up often using their own recorded voices alongside electronic soundscapes combining field recordings, found/archive sound and original musical compositions. Through this they explore how sound works to help shape (or fragment) narrative, to highlight the productive tension between presence and absence. From this comes a shared interest in how field recordings can be used to explore the relationship between language and the physical environment.

In late 2019, Tookey and Heslop visited Great Village, Nova Scotia, to spend time in and around the childhood home of the poet Elizabeth Bishop, who lived there after the death of her father, with her grandparents and her mother, who was shortly afterwards committed to a mental hospital. The intention was to build a sound work with the potential for performance made up of Tookey and Heslop's textual responses to the place, and Heslop's sound work developed from field recordings in various locations in and around the Bishop House.

As Helen Tookey explained:

> We used a method of responding to place we describe as 'sounding': building up an artistic relationship with a new place using immediate and site-specific textual responses to the surrounding environment, alongside audio recordings made within the same environment. As poets, we are both inspired by the ways in which Bishop, throughout her writing, uses precise observation together with careful control of tone to explore themes of loss, place and memory. Our work, both individually and collaboratively, has focused on the ways in which past encounters live on in memory, dream and fantasy; the ways in which places, especially those places that could be described as 'post-industrial', hold echoes and memories of their pasts. Our artistic process of sounding attempts to unlock the many overlapping temporalities that exist in a certain place.[1]

Thus taking their bearings from Bishop's own descriptions, and from their responses to the experience of following in her footsteps by inhabiting her environment, Tookey and Heslop were able to bring their own very different memories and associations to bear on a place neither of them had ever visited before.

> We were also interested in exploring thematically the deeper and wider history of the village and surrounding area, especially the layers of its industrial past – the reclamation of the marshland for farming, the development of the shipyards and the lumber trade, the discovery of iron ore and subsequent mining activity – and the traces left in the landscape by all of these. Great Village has a complex history of settlement, displacement, re-settlement and re-placement, and this wider context would form part of our exploration, looking for – and *listening* for – the traces of the past in the present.
>
> *(Ibid.)*

The possibilities of sound as a connection across time, a link between their project and Bishop herself was given an even stronger purpose because of Bishop's own striking use of sound in her prose memoir/short story, 'In the Village'. In this powerful piece, Bishop employs sonic signposts as a structuring principle; here, it is sound, more than any other sensory mode or communicative medium, which holds memory and emotional power.

For Helen Tookey and Martin Heslop, there was a sense – a feeling that grew during their time in the environs of Great Village – that the Bishop House was at the centre of other 'rooms' spreading out from its hub, as it were, in series within the immediate terrain of Great Village. When we find ourselves in new or strange environments, we interrogate the sounds of the places rather like children: everything is potentially significant and strange until it is identified and given a reason. For Tookey this was important. On the morning after their arrival, quite early, she filled a number of pages with first impressions, her personal, unmitigated responses to the place itself.

> I was struck by the tin roof, the silvery sheen of it, the way the light changed on it, like fish scales, but that put me in mind of a high tinsel-like sound, the sort of sound you'd get from a music box.

We each of us listen for connections, and from them we create immediate spontaneous responses, often informed by our individual experience, and past life.

> Another thing that has stuck with me (in relation to sound) is how much it [the Bishop House] reminded me of my grandma's house, particularly because of the way the kitchen floor sounded when you walked on it... my strongest memory, in a way, of my grandma's house is the peculiar sound of the kitchen floor, a kind of high-pitched rattling/vibrating sound when you walked on it, which I feel as though I would recognise anywhere if I heard it again, but find very hard to describe in words. (One reason it always struck me so much is because her house had floorboards, whereas ours was a modern house with a solid floor, so there was no vibration...)
>
> *(Ibid.)*

Meanwhile, much of Heslop's work related to the 'soundings' concept, working on gathered material while still *in* the environment, mixing and manipulating audio from a day's recording, while sitting in the very rooms described so poignantly by Bishop. 'The place itself becomes the musical instrument; it is composition, shaping, and you can do that *in situ* because the headphones make a room themselves, don't they? You put them on, and somehow they build a world around you.'[2] Much of the relationship between his sound, and the words they both shaped while in Great Village, came from an almost surreal sense of a house that seemed strangely mobile.

> We both felt disorientated; the building was full of windows, and this, combined with the fact that it was on the corner of a main road, gave us the feeling that it had the ability to turn when you weren't aware!
>
> *(Ibid.)*

It all added to the known history of the place, and its dark connection with the disintegrating mental health of Bishop's mother. Working in the actual rooms where this drama had played out a century earlier was a potent experience. Some rooms are innocent, until we learn their past; imaginative sound comes often from the power of suggestion, and association. Interviewing a space, the sound recordist hears first the space itself, but with the potential for this to be the bed of a rediscovery of its narrative through sonic dramatisation.

Wordless Dramas

A journalistic, news-based documentary may seek answers to questions, whereas the aim of an impressionistic, sound painting feature might often be to pose *new* questions, and create a sense of wonder, even awe in the listener's mind. For the BBC radio producer Sara Jane Hall, it is 'the same awe I felt the very first time I turned on a tape recorder and moved from one room to another, and then played it back. Simply magical – detective ears tuning into sounds I couldn't name.'[3]

In March 2019, Hall collaborated with the composer, performer and sound artist Nathaniel Mann to make a remarkable edition of the BBC Radio 3 strand *Between the Ears* on board a giant container ship – the *Maribo Maersk* – in Gdansk shipyard, called *Container Ship Karaoke*. The programme was built around two linked themes, the human and the industrial, with Mann as a musician making the connection between the ancient tradition of sea shanties among sailors, and the modern equivalent, the presence on almost all container vessels of karaoke machines as onboard entertainment, to help alleviate the boredom of spending many months at sea. Alongside this poignant thread, Mann and Hall explored the acoustic world of the ship itself, attaching contact microphones to various surfaces, from the engine room to the 'Monkey Island', the platform above the bridge, discovering sonorities and rhythms hidden behind the reverberating metal walls. The crash of containers as they were loaded conveyed the very awe that Hall mentioned; the ship itself became a cross between a colossal percussive instrument and a living creature. Just as the huge drum sound played by percussionist Hal Blaine in the Simon and Garfunkel song 'The Boxer' was created by Blaine using an open lift shaft to establish the depth of resonance, so here we heard sounds in which metal canisters of great size interacted with a space which was both inhuman, and to the ear and mind, almost unimaginably huge.

> Hearing the whine, shout, squeal, kaboom! of one single container shooting down into the bowels below the deck – many storeys deep – landing with a thud that shook the entire ship, followed by a series of ricochets that made everything shudder in waves, was beyond belief. It never ceased the whole time we were there. It ended up being a heartbeat, a touchstone, a reminder of where we were. The crew didn't even hear it anymore as it is in their background noise 24 hours a day when in port. But to us this environment was deeply unfamiliar, a place that was mysterious and magical, full of strange corridors, metal staircases, heavy doors and endless new decks.
>
> *(Ibid.)*

These sounds, juxtaposed with the comparative fragility and human vulner-
ability of crew members as they spoke of homesickness and loved ones missed
while at sea for up to five months, created a counterpoint that ultimately became
pure composition. At its heart were the stories of those long months away, the
image of empty seas creating a growing sense of the shape of the world, while
the songs of karaoke the men sang, and Nathaniel's own interaction with human
voices inside the body of a machine, gave a sense of living cells within a much
bigger organism: Jonah in the belly of the whale. What made the piece so rich
in terms of the pictures it created was this human music in its strange harmony
with the *musique concrete*, and crucially the exploration of sonic detail, the mix
of voices from men and the ship itself. As they moved around, Hall and Mann's
microphones questioned specific details, so that 'the sounds under the surface felt
like overheard mutterings', and the overall effect was to fill 'a space in the listener's
imagination with Esher-like stairways, corridors, decks and mess-rooms, sound
floating around us in a constant hum' (ibid.). Most of us will never find ourselves
within such a unique space, but *Container Ship Karaoke* is both a piece of narrative
sound art and an archetype for active and creative listening. This is what sound can
do, by employing the auditory imagination of the listener as a complicit member
of the creative process to provide a picture that may or may not be literally what
the producers saw, but which will nevertheless contain its own absolute personal
truth. In the process of sound gathering, the makers asked questions of the ship
rather as a musician explores an instrument to discover what else it can do. To use
another analogy, they took on the roles of diagnostic surgeons, as Nathaniel Mann
explained:

> We boarded the container ship with a set of tools which would let us capture
> and convey these hidden and descriptive sounds. Rather than standard Piezo
> 'contact microphones', which use tiny Piezo crystals to translate vibrations
> travelling through a surface into electric sound (but which also often intro-
> duce a distinctive acoustic signature of their own), my tool of choice was
> the AKG C411 instrument microphone, used in much the same way as a
> contact-mic. The difference is that these are tiny condenser microphones,
> which like most standard microphones, receive airborne vibrations, effect-
> ively holding your listening ear to the sound source. On the container ship
> we used two at once, hard-panned left and right, to create more interesting
> stereo images. This simple set-up meant we could roam the interior of the
> ship and its engines like doctors with stethoscopes, interrogating surfaces,
> seeking out secret sounds.[4]

Such specifics of using a kind of interview technique on inanimate objects reminds
us that sound, particularly in such circumstances, is built of palpable vibrations, and
it is a quality of whole-body listening that in extremer cases can prove remarkably profound. Within the ship, they found 'frenetic staccato rhythms, vibrations

and frictions caused by unseen plates or loose screws, as washers and bolts rubbed together, rattled and shook loose again; regular, mantric pulses, with infinite micro-vibrations' (ibid.). The particularity of these microphones' attentions also helped Hall and Mann to perceive the ship as a whole; as tiny electric ears; recording permitted the programme-makers to hear the heaving of cranes and the slamming of the loading containers as they resonated down through the ship's hull, along its arteries and veins and into the ringing corridors of its very depths, a kind of 'found' percussion concerto. Sometimes they would, like sonic archaeologists, locate and isolate unexpected sounds; what might appear to be a solid steel floor would reveal the rushing of liquid beneath them, as a network of pipes and drainage betrayed itself to the questing microphones:

> There was the peculiar joy of discovering more liquid sounds, those of the sewage processing unit behind an imposing solid surface, what appears to be a sterile mechanical box in retro lime-green and cream pastel hues, but which gave way to joyful sloshing, swirling and gurgling.
>
> *(Ibid.)*

There are times in audio production and sound art when the ambiguity of certain sounds can work to dramatic effect, while at others, emotional response requires clarity and understanding. In a play, for example, location sound may be a key part of the narrative, or indeed, as in the well-known 1978 BBC radio production of *The Revenge*, it may BE the narrative. This 'play without words' by Andrew Sachs, produced for BBC Radio 3 by Glyn Dearman,[5] grew out of a dissatisfaction in Sachs's mind about what he saw as some of the failings of radio drama at the time: a failure too often to make pictures in the mind of anything other than that of a group of actors huddled around a studio microphone. Using binaural microphones and exclusively location-based recordings, he and Dearman created a work in which the sound gave the listener all the narrative they needed, a drama of approximately twenty-five minutes which was designed to be listened to ideally on headphones. The piece has been greatly discussed and critiqued over the years, but in spite of certain shortcomings, it remains a remarkable experiment, particularly for its time. Part of its strength is its ability to interrogate location to the point that the 'sets' upon which the story is played out are clearly 'visible' to the mind's eye. In order that this result should be achieved, close attention had to be paid to every 'shot' in a very real parallel with filmic technique. In works such as *The Revenge*, however, the audience becomes a participant as opposed to an observer, and as a result, the action as it unfolds prints the action and locations on the memory. Pallassmaa writes of what he calls 'acoustic intimacy', a phrase that would seem to be ideally suited to listening to radio and other creative audio: 'Hearing structures and articulating the experience and understanding of space. We are not normally aware of the significance of hearing in spatial experience, although sound often provides the temporal continuum in which visual impressions are embedded' (Pallasmaa, p. 53). In an article relating radio and architecture, Evi Karathanasopoulou develops this idea, with particular reference to the wordless narrative of *The Revenge*:

> Sachs has achieved a… type of aural intimacy that is largely connected to space and the particular sonic landscapes that the protagonist inhabits… Indeed, all the spaces in *The Revenge* are loaded with emotional significance, for example a prison, a home, a town street, a river.
>
> *(Karathanasopolou, p. 128)*

In doing so, the programme makers' microphone asks questions of the space, seeking emotive information of its various reverberations, as the air sends messages from the surfaces and volumes of the locations. Karathanasopolou identifies in the experience of audio

> a tension between the interior and the exterior… Radio happens through the intimate superimpositions of three spaces: the physical space that the listener inhabits; the space that the radio producer creates through recording and editing; and the indefinable space within the listener's head deriving from and within her imagination.
>
> *(Ibid.)*

This is not so far removed from the sound experiences encountered in such places as the strange sound world of Hal Saflieni. The ability of sound to exploit the willingness of a listener to suspend disbelief, transforms their inner auditory world through suggestion to their own personal soundstage. By so doing it links to the concept of audio in the form of radio, as an invisible medium transported through air, a quality that was to its pioneers, almost a supernatural force. As Steven Waller of the University of Virginia has said of the Malta explorations,

> the auditory illusion that the echoed sound is coming from within the rock is consistent with the many myths describing the echo spirits as being trapped within the rock. Furthermore, there are legends associated with rock art describing supernatural portals through the rock from which sound can be heard to emanate.
>
> *(Waller, p. 100)*

These dramas, whether originating from the buried past, or contemporary sound stories, have at their creative heart, a mysterious and elemental power over the imagination.

New spaces offer us the opportunity of listening with an ear uncoloured by experience and familiarity. It is important to be aware and ready for such moments as and when they occur, because they are situations that may only proffer themselves but once, like the first hearing of a piece of music that makes an instant impression, and to which we will return often, although never quite with that first innocent ear. First hearings matter more than perhaps we know, and seeking them out consciously, interrogating rooms in a search for their meanings and voices, can be extremely illuminating. We may bring our own agenda; most people who visit a literary or musical shrine will arrive armed with foreknowledge of what once went on in that place: the environment is already 'loaded' before we even start to focus our hearing on its presence. In other situations we may find ourselves flung into an alien environment of noise, reverberation and thundering resonance, such as the bowels of a great cargo ship in the act of consuming its charges, where we must learn to 'read' the sound and acoustics quickly with the sense that survival may depend upon it. Equally there are subterranean worlds through which we stumble in the dark, looking for signs, and hearing our own sounds coming back to us, eerily changed, as we seek to uncover what lost lives heard, and what it meant to them. At the heart of all auditory relationships with space is the meaning we invest in them ourselves through living and association. Coming back to a once-familiar house after many years, to sense it changed by new habitation, occupied by other lives, one inevitably pauses and listens for clues. At first, nothing seems the same, and then a footfall triggers the creak of a floorboard, and the familiar sound opens a door in the mind: 'That board creaked when we were here…' Little wonder that Thomas Hardy wrote in his poem 'Silences':

> …The rapt silence of an empty house
>> Where oneself was born,
>> Dwelt, held carouse
> With friends, is of all silences most forlorn!
>> *(Hardy, p. 865)*

Forlorn it may be, but the sounds of empty, unadorned space may be, as we shall come to consider in the final chapter, the most significant, salutary and honest of all: rooms in which we have no choice but to examine the resonating reality behind the context of living.

Notes

1 Helen Tookey, interview with the author, March 2020. Reproduced with permission.
2 Martin Heslop, interview with the author, March 2020. Reproduced with permission.
3 Sara Jane Hall, communication with the author, February 2020. Reproduced with permission.
4 Nathaniel Mann, communication with the author, February 2020. Reproduced with permission.
5 See Seán Street. *The Poetry of Radio: The Colour of Sound*. Abingdon: Routledge, 2012.

References

Eneix, Linda C. *Listening for Ancient Gods.* Myakka City, FL: OTS Foundation, 2016.

Hardy, Thomas. *The Complete Poems of Thomas Hardy.* Ed. James Gibson. London: Macmillan, 1979.

Hendy, David. *Noise: A Human History of Sound and Listening.* London: Profile Books, 2013.

Jamie, Kathleen. *Findings.* London: Sort of Books, 2005.

Karathansopolou, E. 'Atmosphere in Radio and Architecture: Using *The Revenge* Radio Play in Interdisciplinary Teaching as a Means to Understand Notions of Abstraction and the Tensions between Materiality and Immateriality in Building Physical and Imagined Spaces', *Radio Journal: International Studies in Broadcast and Audio Media*, 17:1, 2019, 113–29, oi:10.1386/rajo.17.1.113_1.

Pallasmaa, Juhani. *The Eyes of the Skin: Architecture and the Senses.* Chichester: Wiley, 2012.

Reznikoff, Iegor. 'On Primitive Elements of Musical Meaning', *JMM – The Journal of Music and Meaning*, 3, Fall 2004/Winter 2005, Section 2. www.musicandmeaning.net/issues/showArticle.php?artID=3.2.

Stroud, Katya. 'Ħal Saflieni Hypogeum: Acoustic Myths and Science', in Linda C. Eneix (ed.), *Archaeoacoustics: The Archaeology of Sound. Proceedings of the 2014 Conference in Malta.* Myakka City, FL: OTS Foundation, 2014, pp. 37–43.

Tibble, J.W. (ed.) *The Poems of John Clare, Vol. II.* London: J.M. Dent, 1935.

Waller, Steven J. 'Auditory Illusions of Rock Art and Stonehenge', in Linda C. Eneix (ed.), *Archaeoacoustics: The Archaeology of Sound. Proceedings of the 2014 Conference in Malta.* Myakka City, FL: OTS Foundation, 2014, pp. 99–106.

8

THE ROOMS WE MAKE AND THE ROOMS WE ARE

This Place, Here and Now

The Swiss architect Peter Zumthor placed a quotation on the wall of his office; some might expect it to be a statement by a great name from the architectural past, such as Vitruvius or Kircher, but in fact it was a sentence by the French musicologist André Boucourechliev, about the Russian composer Igor Stravinsky:

> Radical diatonism, forceful and distinctive rhythmical pronunciation, melodic clarity, harmonies plain and severe, a piercing radiance of tone colour, and finally, the simplicity and transparency of his musical fabric, the stability of his formal structures.
>
> *(Zumthor, p. 21)*

Explaining the reasoning behind his enthusiasm for these words, Zumthor told his staff: 'That is how we've got to work!... What it tells me is something about atmosphere: the composer's music has that quality too, the ability to touch us – to touch me – within seconds of listening' (ibid.). It is highly significant that such an architect as Zumthor should choose a sound metaphor as his mantra. It helps us too, because it enables us to focus on the sound around us, to send the attention out beyond the noisy room that is our own consciousness. In 1976, David Kemp, working at the Ear Clinic of University College, London, demonstrated the existence of the phenomenon of otoacoustic emissions, recordable sounds actually generated from within the inner ear. These are caused by the motion of the cochlea's hair cells as they respond to auditory stimulation, sounds arising in the ear canal when, paradoxically, the tympanum receives vibrations transmitted backwards through the middle ear from the cochlea. Today, these sounds can be diagnosed in order to treat patients with hearing disorders. Thus it seems that even before my brain can enter the conversation, the ear is sending signals of its own. Add this to the fact that when I enter an anechoic studio, I hear myself in the form of the whistle of my nervous system and the hum and pulse of my blood stream, I come to realise how noisy I am, and how much work I need to do in order to quieten my own personal room, even before I begin to explore other spaces. The issue is infinite and intimate at the same time. Every person on the planet *is* their own room, and carries their own sonic space with them throughout their lives, subjectively interpreting the physical rooms of the world through which that particular life takes them. Even allowing for this, there are less tenuous spaces of which each of us is aware: the world of the sub-aqua, countless geographic spaces where we will never go, and places where sound changes, or changes those who enter it.

Every national and regional culture is its own room, a place in which familiarity and habit may make us feel at home and part of an essence of belonging, or conversely excluded and a stranger. Language or dialect, music or a soundscape may be the first symptoms of entering someone else's room. Thus the sound of a room may segregate you, if your dialect, accent or language betray you, as coming from outside the chosen tribe. The terrain of our homeland forms a room that infiltrates deeply into our psyche, manifesting itself in terms of the expressions of language and music. We can only be where we are, and beyond that, all is imagination and memory. This may be the most important concept of all, because it enables each one of us the capacity to be both rooted in a specific place, and psychically everywhere at one and the same time. To start, listen to THIS place, HERE and NOW, because whatever we do, say, make or record, it has to happen in a place, within air. That air may be still or violently swept by weather; whatever its mood, it affects ours, because it is where what happens, *happens*. To leave the recorder running after we have left is at once to gain evidence of sound outside and beyond our immediate awareness, removing the vital sense of the 'here and now' that generates our relationship with a space when we are present within it. We are visitors everywhere, and our temporary presence in a place is only a frame in the film of that environment's existence. A room will have a dialogue with us, but when we are gone, it will resume its own monologue, unheard, awaiting its next interaction. Barry Truax has written of this:

> Above all, sounds exist in time, and to a large extent, they create and influence our sense of time. Therefore it is not surprising that our sense of the character or coherence of an environment is closely tied to the temporal relationships exhibited by sound. These relationships include both the sounds' internal evolution over time and their patterns on different time scales, from those at the short-term memory level to the largest circadian and seasonal variations. Because we normally pass through environments, we seldom become aware of the larger rhythms and cycles they exhibit. Nothing is more revealing to the soundscape analyst than

to monitor the changes in an acoustically rich environment over some lengthy period of time.

(*Truax, p. 65*)

Most of these environments are constructs, either built spaces, or spaces affected by the creation of objects that themselves generate variations in the soundscape. For an architect, there are a huge range of considerations that govern design, which in turn are developed within the context of specific needs and circumstances. When I choose a house to live in, or a space in which to perform, study, contemplate or even simply to listen, my selection may be affected by aesthetic considerations: the arrangement and size of room, the location, the view and so on. Yet these walls are the end product of a process, and have come into being through a range of practical decisions, some of which may have involved close attention to acoustics. On the other hand, I may have commissioned the build myself, in which case I will have perhaps been more actively involved in the physical realisation of my requirements. The architect has thus a range of pressures upon him or her, with the additional issue of regulatory limitations: 'The residential environment has the most stringent requirements for noise control/abatement because of the sensitivities required of domestic living, including sleep, and with sleep deprivation in particular.'[1] The Australian architect Gordon Tench summarises these considerations, and points to the increasing importance of sound as an issue both for home owners and local authorities alike:

> In the first consideration architects apply statutory building standards such as the British Standards, which apply to various aspects of building/development, including noise control. These are generally considered minimum standards that cover various aspects of the built environment, including noise abatement and control, to provide for peaceful enjoyment of people's own property. Where possible or demanded, these are exceeded, arising from client demands for enhanced requirements of noise control.
>
> (*Ibid.*)

Both within, and beyond domestic situations, architects are increasingly adopting innovative designs in terms of shapes, particularly, as Tench points out, in locations where for professional purposes, the room is sound critical:

> Hard surfaces of parallel walls have the effect of amplifying reverberation and it is not uncommon in the areas where this is considered a serious problem, for buildings and building elements to be constructed without parallel surfaces, in conjunction with dynamic sound control systems (i.e. the ability to adjust the position and size of absorptive surfaces) to control reflected sound. This is most evident in music studios for example, where a range of acoustic controls such as perforated acoustic linings can

be employed to mitigate reflected sound. Any window openings, whilst double-glazed, are generally constructed so that the glass panes are angled, and acoustic absorption is provided in the gap to avoid vibrations transferring through these glazed elements.

(Ibid.)

The sensations we absorb from these seemingly permanent places transfer their presence into an inner space, where they may become the stages upon which are played out stories and fantasies. The shape, decor and circumstances of physical space become a part of us by simply surrounding us, but we can also relate to places we have never been through imagination, and through the knowledge of what it *feels* like to inhabit the air of a particular place. We are all figures in the landscape, as were those who walked it before us.

Phantom Rooms

Earlier in this book I described stepping into a room full of sound, and being first aware of the sound rather than the physical space; this is of course a common experience to anyone who relies entirely on sound for their sense of place. John Hull, in analysing in intimate detail the experience of going blind in his book *Touching the Rock*, powerfully illustrates ideas of sound as a dynamic force, affecting the passive listener:

> The creatures emitting the noise have to engage in some activity. They have to scrape, bang, hit, club, strike surface upon surface, impact, make their vocal chords vibrate. They must take the initiative in announcing their presence to me. For my part, I have no power to explore them. I cannot penetrate them or discover them without their active co-operation. They must utter their voice, their sound. It is thus a world which comes to me, which springs into life for me.
>
> *(Hull, p. 73)*

A song is a room we inhabit vocally, instrumentally or aurally, for the duration of our time in it. Our presence within it may be active or passive, as a generating, dynamic force, a respondent through physical action, such as a dancer, or as an active listener. Tune to a favourite podcast, and you enter an imaginative room. Unlike a live radio show, where you may have come into the midst of a discussion, it is a room made by the producer and yourself, and you have right of entry whenever you wish, and as often as you like. Podcasts in this sense, we might argue, have always existed in one form or another. There have been inhabitable rooms since there were ideas themselves. Insofar as they occupy mental space, we access them in the form of poems, articles, essays, short stories or song lyrics, each of these is a kind of podcast that began as a thought. Here, we come to one of the strangest things about rooms of all, because while we acknowledge that they are places of occupation, at another imaginative level, we may consider that our presence in them does not have to be physical at all. Any human experience is a room made of time and event, and by absorbing a fictional story, whether it be in print or as a piece of visual art, we enter through a doorway into the suspension of our disbelief. We do this each time we engage with an imaginative narrative in any form, as Pallasmaa points out:

> Novels transport us through cities invoked by the magic of the writer's word. The rooms, squares and streets of a great writer are as vivid as any we have visited; the invisible cities of Italo Calvino have forever enriched the urban geography of the world... We *become* citizens of mid-19th century St Petersburg through the incantations of Dostoyevsky. We *are* in the room of Raskolnikov's shocking double murder... The streets in great paintings continue around corners and past the edges of the picture frame into the invisible with all the intricacies of life.
>
> *(Pallasmaa, p. 74)*

A poem is the essence of a room, a shape on the page and in the mind. It is a physical as well as a conceptual object; I enter a known text as I would come into a familiar room. I might turn to it *because* I know it, and remind myself of insights which may have been forgotten. As Peter Murphy has written: 'Poems are ideas, and they are also ink. The inkiness of poems allies them with the crumbling material world, but their ideas can make them seem permanent, free of time's grip' (Murphy, p. xv). That 'inkiness' is the medium through which the silent sound of an idea translates itself into the physical world, enabling it to be vocalised, shared sonically, or transformed back into silent sound within the mind of the reader. They are also portable, these sound rooms. I open a book as I would open a door, and move to a certain, much-thumbed page, a familiar room of choice. Yet just as, however many times we move house, we remember past beloved rooms, and can summon the idea of the sound of them, likewise we can carry our own favourite poem or song with us through memory, ready to open the door at any time, wherever we may be. So the poem or song does *not* vanish. We may read new poems and learn to love new songs, but the *inkiness* of the physical world prints itself conceptually on the fabric of who we are and how we got here.

So a poem is a physical thing, but also a sonic airborne space that can exist in memory, and would continue to do so, even were the tangible text in all its manifestations to be lost. In this, it is like all creative works, be they music, declaimed speech or even apparently silent objects such as paintings and sculpture. Once seen and engaged with, when remembered at a future time, we may call not only the thing itself to mind, but also the feelings it engendered, and a mental picture of the room in which we encountered it, sometimes down to the very sounds that pertained at the time. As we read a poem, we become aware not only of it as a kind of room, but also of the shapes of its construction: the stanzas, so distinct in their perspective within the overall story that they become their own rooms. Cresswell has expressed the physicality of a poem thus:

> The poem can be thought of as a kind of archipelago. Just as islands in an archipelago are separated by water yet linked by trade and ecosystems, each stanza in the poem is spatially separated from the next, yet still simultaneously linked through the logic of sentences.
>
> *(Cresswell, in Magrane et al., p. 176)*

I might substitute islands connected by water for a building full of rooms, linked by halls, stairs and passageways in the mind, but otherwise, the analogy is apposite.

When we read silently to ourselves, we engage sonically with images implied by a writer through a series of codes. Put simply, because we *see* words, we have the capacity to imagine, and through that capacity, the potential to create our own internal mental sound world. Engaging with the text of a long-dead writer, we participate in a form of imaginative resurrection; the text connects us to the human life that brought it into existence, in real time, as Mark Doty suggested in his book *Still Life with Oysters and Lemon*:

> The form, spoken, breathes something of that life out into the world again. It restores a human presence; hidden in the lines… is the writer's breath, are the turns of thought and of phrase, the habits of saying, which make those words unmistakable. And so the result is a permanent intimacy; we are brought into relationship with the perceptual character, the speaking voice, of someone we probably never knew, someone no one can know now, except in this way.
>
> *(Doty, p. 50)*

In modern times, media connections mean that we may have heard the *actual* voice of a writer, and in certain cases, when that voice is distinctive or idiosyncratic, the memory conjures the sound as we read a printed text. A room is a sonic place in which I find myself, a place in which we live with ourselves. If that place exists firstly as sound, it follows that its existence within this context is an event in time and space, leading us to the *idea* of a room. On the other hand, we might agree that the sound also grows out of the idea. A novel is a room, or a series of rooms we occupy as we read it, just as it was for the author during the process of writing. There are works of literature that began their existence out of loneliness, because their author had no one to talk to, and their genesis was in rooms we now by implication inhabit while the writer's work is in communion with us. Many readers become engrossed in the imaginary world of a book for the same reason. As we begin to read, and listen, we accept an invitation to enter the author's room, and once inside this imaginative space, growing accustomed to their voice, we join them on journeys that may take us together to other rooms, hearing other voices. As Jeanette Winterson has put it:

> Reading is not a passive act. Engaged in a book, in company with the writer, the mind can roam where it will. Such freedom to roam reminds us that body and mind both need exercise and activity, and that neither the mind or the body can cope with confinement. And if the body has to cope with confinement, then all the more reason to have developed a mind that knows how to roam.
>
> *(Winterson, in Shepherd, p. 117)*

The imagined sounds of real or fictional spaces may have the scope to create an almost limitless landscape or seascape, or they may take us no further than to another room. What is the entirety of Marilynne Robinson's novel *Gilead* but a man talking to the reader, ostensibly through his son, as it were, face to face? For the duration, we are in a room together, with walls made of imagination, and in the case of *Gilead*, a fictional room in Iowa, a study where the seventy-six-year-old Reverend John Ames sits and writes a long letter – the length of the book itself – to his little boy, looking back over his life and that of the child himself, from the vantage point of 1956. Ames is nearing death, and the book is, as James Wood has written, 'less a novel than a species of religious writing, and Reverend Ames's entries are a recognisable American form, the Emersonian essay, poised between homily and home, religious exercise and naturalism' (Wood, p. 448). The work has virtually no dialogue, and the only scenes that occur are through events recorded in the diary entries of Ames himself, capturing memories. It is a quiet book, reflecting vividly the gentle spirit of its central character and narrator. Yet it is full of subtle sound, transmitted through memory. While the predominant tone may be the voice of Ames, that voice speaks so clearly that we feel we would recognise it if we were to hear it on the other end of the telephone line. We picture his space, and its sound, in the context of the house in which he sits, the timber resonances and the footsteps on boards, surrounded by Iowa pressing in from outside. We learn that Ames loves baseball, but in old age it is the radio that provides the pictures:

> Sometimes I could make out half a play, and then static, and then a crowd roaring, a flat little sound, almost static itself, like that empty sound in a seashell. It felt good to me to imagine it, like working out some intricate riddle in my mind, planetary motion. If the ball is drifting toward left field and there are runners on first and third, then – moving the runners and the catcher and the shortstop in my mind. I loved to do that, I can't explain why.
>
> *(Robinson, p. 50)*

Anyone who has listened to sport, rather than watched it, will understand exactly the pictorial nature of Ames's experience. We enter the radio's room somewhere between reality and the abstract, and in so doing we gain a kind of interactive imaginative power that is denied to the person who observes the game on TV. In the town of Gilead, and in particular within the house itself, we are subject to worlds within worlds, at the centre of a life. The sound may be implicit, but the mind hears it:

> You come in reeking of evening air, with your eyes bright and fingers pink and cold, too beautiful in the candlelight for my old eyes. The cold has silenced all the insects. The dark seems to make us speak softly, like gentle conspirators. Your mother says the grace and butters your bread.
>
> *(Ibid., p. 277)*

It is wistful, poetic and eloquent, and at the heart of it is a voice talking quietly, on and on, a voice we hear speaking to us from its time, a real time albeit through an imagined man and his story. In her book *Voices and Books in the English Renaissance*, Jennifer Richards takes us closer to the personal spaces of the past by giving us insights into the classrooms of Renaissance England; in so doing, she movingly puts our personal memory alongside the ghosts of generations who came before. She does so, initially, by way of a picture book for children, *Orbis Sensualium Pictus* (*The World of Things in Pictures*, 1657) by the Moravian educationalist Johann Comenius. The book shows us life in the classroom offering instructions for the process by which we 'maketh words', and it 'teacheth how to utter, write, put together and part them rightly… as it were, paint'. Richards opens a door onto the human sound of the past, be it in school, the church or on the page itself. We are familiar with texts consciously created for performance in the works of Marlowe, Shakespeare, Jonson and the rest. Here is the voice of the silent reader, who sometimes articulates a personal response, or adds a thought here and there in the margins of existing texts.

Books and other written texts are more than objects: they are vehicles for thoughts that began, as Murphy and Doty reminded us, in the breathing world. So what happens when we vocalise a text? We restore its mortality, its temporality, its physical origins, including an abstract idea of its creator and the context in which it was made. We make a sound of it that passes away from us and is gone, moves on, just as we do, leaving a fixed mark on the page which was our prompt – the author's text – with the possible graffiti and addenda of our own, to be reinterpreted by some other future reader. When we read out loud, we are speaking the written word, and voicing the original thoughts, on behalf of the author. Thus in the sixteenth and seventeenth centuries, the eye and the tongue were being brought into alignment through the medium of printed books, and the classroom is a key location for the demonstration of this. The church is another; to the educated reader, there was the opportunity for reading a text to which they had been already introduced by the voice of the clergy, and in so doing, to examine it – turn back the page and reread – at leisure. Having thus been mentally 'recorded', there was the further possibility of sharing the words and giving them one's own vocal interpretation, as in this example, quoted by Jennifer Richards, from the journal of Lady Margaret Hoby, writing in September 1599:

> The Lordes Day 30 After a privat praier I went to church wher I hard the word Preached, and received the sacrementes to my Comfort: after I had given thankes and dined, I walked a whill, and then went to church, whence, after I had hard Catacizing and sarmon, I returned home and wret notes in my Bible, and talked of the sarmon and good thinges with Mrs Ormston: then I went to praier, after to supper, then to repetecion of the wholl daies exersice and praiers, hard one of the men reade of the book of marters, and so went to bed.
>
> *(Richards, p. 132)*

Thus it is that we gain an understanding of how worship in church was reinforced and augmented by domestic further reading – or rereading – and discussion at home. From this, our imagination, if we so desire, may play with the idea of acoustics, and the style of declamation: firstly rhetorical, allowing for the liquid sounds of the great building, then contrasted with the intimacy of the household situation, with its own acoustic presence. In both cases, the print is transformed by sharing, into what we might now describe as in some ways a similar experience to that of a talking book.

Resonating Canvas

Every physical artistic image – be it a painting, a photograph or a piece of sculpture – is its own sound room. Next to one another in the Walker Art Gallery in Liverpool, there are two contrasting paintings that are brimful of the sounds of their respective rooms. One is a picture by William Hogarth (1697–1764,) a depiction of a theatrical scene, and thus, art capturing art. It is a portrait of the great actor David Garrick, painted between 1742 and 1745. In it, Garrick is shown at one of the most dramatic moments of Shakespeare's *Richard III*, in his tent on Bosworth Field, the night before the battle that will cost him his life. It is the precise moment in which Richard awakens from a nightmare: 'The lights burn blue! Is it not dead midnight? / Cold fearful drops hang upon my trembling flesh' (Shakespeare, *Richard III*, Act 5, Scene III). It is a picture of many layers: we are observing a performance on a stage, a scene showing us a room, in which the fictionalised representation of a real person is in the act of a dramatic portrayal, speaking words created by the playwright. The depiction goes further, because while we are imaginatively 'in' Richard's tent, the painting is itself providing an *idea* of the original structure, a re-creation conceived by Garrick's set designer, and perhaps further embellished by Hogarth for the purposes of the picture. This is really the first great theatrical portrait, and at the same time it is taking us into a space that actually existed once in some form, in its own right. Hogarth is encouraging the viewer to 'listen' to the words in the room, the night ambience outside the tent, and through all this, to enter into the reality of an historical happening, rather than simply a performance on stage.

In contrast, a painting by the French-Austrian painter Jacob van Schuppen (1670–1751) called 'The Guitar Player' shows a family group, believed to be William Waldegrave, private physician to King James II at his court in exile in France, with Waldegrave's wife and niece, and their pet dog. We know that Waldegrave commissioned a portrait from van Schuppen in 1700, the year before his death, and we may assume that this is that same picture. It is a scene full of gentle imagined sound and affection. Playing the guitar was a popular courtly pursuit in France in the early eighteenth century, particularly suitable for accompanying singing, and Waldegrave was himself known as a celebrated performer on the instrument. On a table, there is a music book, open at a song, and Waldegrave's wife, sitting close beside him, looks to be in the midst of singing to his accompaniment as he plays his small guitar, while the little girl dances to the tune. In the physical world, we make and hear music, note by note, each note as it falls being a minute expression of the present moment, before fading into the past. Here are real people, shown enjoying a domestic pastime, with a favourite song on their lips. It is a sonic moment held, the ghost of a tune heard, as they look out at us from a day more than three hundred years ago. Its lost sound moves through time to enter our space; we might even leave the gallery, mentally 'hearing' a tune of the time, prompted by the image of notes on the table, restoring the idea of the sound to the temporality of air, and the three- (or perhaps in this instance, even four-) dimensional world.

As the Waldegraves sang together that day, they were physically in their drawing room, but at the same time, for the duration of the song, they were together in the emotional room of the music they created as depicted – and perhaps idealised – by the artist. Our relationship with music is deep, subjective and personal. We each make or hear the same notes, but we may build our own internal scenarios from them. For example, when I listen with eyes closed to Ravel's *Introduction and Allegro* for harp and string quartet, I might create my personal imagined sunlit spring garden, perhaps a place half-remembered from childhood. On the other hand, if I play a recording of Bartók's *Music for Strings, Percussion and Celesta*, I have the capacity to enter a very different space, full of shadows, a strange, haunted terrain. Here is my garden, but now imagined in some bleak, post-apocalyptic time. At least, that is how it seems to me today, because I am currently in a mood room built by this music and my answering imagination. It may change according to circumstance, just as the light alters in a physical space through days, evenings and nights, across time. Whatever the interpretation, it belongs to each individual listener alone. There are no wrong answers here, because the composer, who gave the music to the musicians, who in turn have given it to me, has allowed me to take it into my own mind, where it becomes my internal room. Listening on headphones, I create an all-inclusive space inside, whilst by listening on speakers, my physical room joins in with its acoustic, as the music touches the walls and colours the air with its volume, timbre and pitch for a few minutes.

Likewise, by entering the sound world of a painting, we do so through the window of its canvas. The best work of the painter Paul Klee (1879–1940) articulates sound through colour, and indeed his avowed aim was to extemporise spontaneously with paint in the same way that a musician can expand a theme: 'One day I must be able to improvise freely on the keyboard of colours: the row of watercolours in my paint box' (Klee, p. 873). The idea of a paint box offering a representation of a keyboard is an attractive one. Klee was deeply aware of the parallels between art and music, in particular, Mozart and Bach: 'As yet they defy analysis. It is certain that both art forms are defined by time' (ibid., p. 640). The complexity of the issue arises because, in Klee's thinking, music showed him the innermost essence of nature, not its reproduction, and it was this 'room' into which his work was taking him, and which was at once an internal space and a cosmic one.

> By analysing methods of musical composition and converting them into their visual equivalents, Klee achieved a new form – polyphonic painting – in which movement and counter-movement could be visibly demonstrated as an allegory for the reconciliation of conflicts within a superior order
>
> *(Düchting, p. 88)*

The greatest of Klee's work gathers the passing colours and ideas of music and places them before us for contemplation, as he said:

> To lay bare the elements and group them into assembled subdivisions, to dissect and reconstruct into a whole simultaneously at various places, to create a visual polyphony and to bring about stillness by balancing movement, all these are aspects of form and are of great importance for the knowledge of form, but they are not yet art. In the uppermost circle, beyond ambiguity, there lies a final mystery, which the light of our meagre intellect fails to penetrate.
>
> *(Klee, in Günther Regel, p. 65)*

The Sound Memory of a Room

Between the years 1982 and 1988, I made a series of radio programmes with the late Myfanwy Thomas, daughter of the poet Edward Thomas, at her home in the village of Eastbury, Berkshire. Sitting in her living room, we recorded interviews comprising memories of her childhood, and what she recalled of her father (she was seven when he was killed at the Battle of Arras in 1917). As part of those conversations, she read a number of his poems, and listening to those recordings, there is a calm and a gentle ambience that preserves the experience of being in that room. It was what one might call a typical cottage interior, furnished with soft chairs and a sofa, around an open fireplace, unostentatious and timeless; even in the 1980s, it was the sort of rural dwelling interior that her father would have recognised. During one of those visits, Myfanwy gave me a recording of her mother, Helen Thomas, reading from Edward's work. Helen was a great advocate and champion of her husband's poems, and spent much of her life promoting interest in them. The recording was on a privately made ten-inch vinyl disc, and I was struck by the similarity between Helen and Myfanwy's voices. I was also intrigued by the fact that Helen's readings had been made in the very room in which Myfanwy and I held our conversations. I conceived the idea of producing a radio programme in which mother and daughter should be brought back together in one joint reading of the Thomas poems, within the common space of that same room. Helen's recording had been made during the 1960s, and allowing for the passage of time, different recording technology, as well as the pre-digital quality of sound taken directly from the old vinyl, it was possible to obtain a reasonable mix, and Myfanwy's interest in the project, and ability to invoke the presence of Helen, made for an audio experience in which the listener could have the illusion of the two women sitting side by side in that cottage interior, sharing memories and poems. The programme was broadcast in 1987 on LBC Radio.

Helen Thomas died in 1967, and Myfanwy in 2005. Listening to the recording now, I am conscious of the decades that have passed since it was made. Likewise, the day Helen sat down to read the poems in her time has itself grown further and further away. Yet here they both are, united across the years in a single room, and in their pauses, you can hear the place around them, homely and familiar as it was to them when they sat there. There is a connection between the physicality of the place as it existed then, the medium and the sound as artefact, memory and abstract presence in the mind. So it was with the poems themselves, when they were conceived and written down, becoming the objects that in turn became the sounds as read out loud, long after the poet himself had died. As Peter Murphy says, the 'inkiness' of the actual object links us to the moment, and invokes both the sound of the poem as it persists in words, and – imaginatively – the presence that existed within the room where it was made. Likewise, the sound of my recordings passes through the air – different air – and reaches me; meanwhile, somewhere in a cottage in a village in Berkshire, England, there is a room, now perhaps much changed and inhabited by different owners, where these sounds were first made in that air, and recorded.

We return to the idea that a sonic room is temporal as well as physical and historical. It becomes the representation of a period of time in which sound happens and/or happened. Yet that period of time occurs within a physical space; we bring the room of our consciousness back to our moment in time within a place, putting us within its chronology, hearing that instant and its history again. As Judy Lochhead, professor of Music History and Theory at Stony Brook University, New York, has written:

> As happenings and particularities, places 'gather' – knitting together things, feelings, memories, thoughts, and projections. Our experience of places then has not only a sensuous and embodied fullness but also an intrinsically cultural and historical fullness, bearing the traces of those who have and do inhabit them… The listening body engages the world through the fullness of its synaesthesia and kinaesthesia, both taking in and animating sounds. Such bodily inter-animations of listening constitute the sonic places that gather together memories, thoughts, and feelings. Sonic places, like other sorts of places, are inherently meaningful as a consequence of inter-animations between the listening body and the material conditions of place.
> *(Lochhead, p. 686)*

I listen to a song or a voice, or 'hear' a memory, bringing my own imagined presence to the place of sonic origin, with its context of time and weather, mood and health, and combined with my own current physical space. It is while carrying all these criteria that I listen, interpret and make judgements on what I hear there. It is both space and time travel. I have an old vinyl record of Sean O'Casey reading extracts from his plays. It was made at his home at Totnes, Devon on 12 November 1952. At several points in the recording, there is the sound of a distant steam train's whistle, faint, but distinct. Without that sound, there is just O'Casey: the rich timbre, the grain of his voice, the dialect, and through the voice, the characters his mind created in *Juno and the Paycock*, *Pictures in the Hallway* and *Innisfallen, Fare Thee Well*. Generally, in the recording, there are few clues offering a sense of location, until the train sounds somewhere, away in the Devon valley, and there all at once is O'Casey in his time and place. How often in my career have I stopped recording for a moment to allow an extraneous sound to pass because I felt it was intrusive and distracting from an interview or an effect I was seeking to achieve? How I wish I had sometimes allowed the place its voice a little more, and how rewarding have been the times when I listened closely to the environment, and responded to it. For example, there was such an occasion when I was making a programme with the producer Alan Hall about the young World War II pilot poet John Magee, and his famous poem 'High Flight'. We were recording near the place where Magee had been killed when his Spitfire crashed into a Lincolnshire field in 1941. I was voicing a link, and half way through, Alan and I both became aware of a sound. I paused, and overhead, high, very high, was a Spitfire. It must have come from a nearby airfield, one of very few still flying from historic collections. It was an unforgettable moment, so perfect that listeners to the programme might assume it was added as a sound effect, placed deliberately when the programme was mixed later. However, such strange things can happen on location, and when they occur, all we can do is listen and respond. Honour the sound of the room. Allow it to speak.

Post Script: Empty Rooms

Through the spring of 2020, the doors of rooms all over the world began to close, as the Covid-19 virus spread. Public spaces: theatres, galleries, museums, and shopping centres, places of worship and sports arenas, gradually fell silent. We even slammed shut the doors of our countries, and social interaction grew less and less. The places of familiar, gregarious habit became a memory. Roads that had been busy were suddenly quiet: a passing car became something one noticed, and a knock on the door felt like a potential threat. I am writing these final words during that time of self-isolation and uncertainty, and I am reflecting on the journeys and places described in this book. Having begun in the autumn of 2019, and taken for granted the freedom to share space with others, I consider all those rooms again, and how a global catastrophe sonically changed them. At least I have their memory, etched into my imagination, with the back-up of a sound memory card to remind me. Our recorders continue to do what we ask of them, and beside them, we listen. So I have returned in my mind to the Picton Reading Room in Liverpool Central Library, the room in which I sat and wrote the first words of this book, and I remember the tearing sound of Velcro as someone opened a bag that first day… there it is again, playing in memory. Many months have passed since that tiny event happened, but I have no need of the recording I made then to recreate those minutes.

It has not been my intention in writing this book to compartmentalise the sounding world, to package and box sonic experience. Wherever we are, whatever we hear, there are usually peripheral sounds, accidentals and murmurs coming from the room next door. I would wish to suggest, rather, that by focusing on one space at a time, by listening, and then building awareness of the larger aural perspective around it, we might aid our ability to focus on the music of the world as it plays its solos, duets or from time to time joins in as a chorus. I acknowledge the mystery of how it is that imagination allows the replay of things that are no longer there. It is, as Murphy writes, why old poems matter so much:

> Because they show us that people were like us, in the past, even if their likenesses can be discerned only through an exercise in the imagination. Because the effort of connecting with vanished worlds is salutary. Because working out what someone else was thinking is good practice for knowing other people and treating them humanely. Because literacy is a claim against disorder and dissolution, and we need that claim.
>
> *(Murphy, p. 217)*

I would add to that: while I engage with those people, I hear them imaginatively, occupying the spaces that were theirs and that seemed so solid and permanent and reassuring, listening to *their* rooms in *their* time as I do now to mine. Locked down in my own home, I also have time to reflect on the spaces that surround me here and now, and how they sounded the day we moved in, their acoustic so empty and echoing. Was *that* the rooms' definitive sound, the hollow ring of bare floors before the carpets, books, pictures and furniture came, when the spaces were devoid of human accoutrements? We have peopled a cave with the domestic preferences that provide the comforting presence of our possessions, in the process shaping its sound as we changed its décor to our own taste. Nonetheless, it will have its time again without us, a brief moment when the walls ring and the floors resonate in the absence of the objects with which humans surround themselves, before the next temporary tenants come in with the fabric of *their* lives. They too will stay for a while, believing their characteristic sound to belong definitively to the place. They may or may not consciously recognise this auditory world as having their stamp on it, but it will. Yet under it all, there will be a sonic continuity, a constant common denominator. Until the building itself crumbles, it will hold a unique voice that was built into the space itself when the walls first enclosed air. Rooms shape sound, and frame it, but each room retains its own unique sound too. The structure and fabric of every particular space generates a specific sonic character in its individual auditory image. Someone however, must be there to perceive it and sense that presence, to give it meaning, and by being there to hear, inevitably change the voice of the place. Attend to it now. The sound of a room surrounded by its context: atmosphere, moving air, creaking timbers, and you, listening, while from the room outside the door, there comes the sound of music, voices, the weather pressing on the glass, birdsong, time.

Note

1 Gordon Tench, personal communication with the author, 2017. Reproduced with permission.

References

Doty, Mark. *Still Life with Oysters and Lemon*. Boston, MA: Beacon Press, 2002.

Düchting, Hajo. *Paul Klee: Painting Music*. London: Prestel, 2016.

Hull, John M. *Touching the Rock*. London: SPCK, 1990.

Klee, Paul. Ed. Felix Klee. *The Diaries of Paul Klee*. London: University of California Press, 1964.

Lochhead, Judy I. 'Music Places: Imaginative Transports of Listening', in Mark Grimshaw-Aagaard, Mags Walther-Hansen and Martin Knakkergaard, *The Oxford Handbook of Sound and Imagination, Volume 1*. Oxford: Oxford University Press, 2019, pp. 683–700.

Murphy, Peter. *The Long Public Life of a Short Private Poem: Reading and Remembering Thomas Wyatt*. Stanford, CA: Stanford University Press, 2019.

Pallasmaa, Juhani. *The Eyes of the Skin: Architecture and the Senses*. Chichester: Wiley, 2012.

Regel, Günther (ed.). *Paul Klee: Kunste-Lehre*. Leipzig: Reclam Leipzig, 1991.

Richards, Jennifer. *Voices and Books in the English Renaissance: A New History of Reading.* Oxford: Oxford University Press, 2019.

Robinson, Marilynne. *Gilead.* London: Virago, 2005.

Shepherd, Nan. *The Living Mountain.* Afterword by Jeanette Winterson. Edinburgh: Canongate Books, 2014.

Truax, Barry. *Acoustic Communication.* Norwood, NJ: Ablex Publishing, 1984.

Wood, James. *Serious Noticing: Selected Essays.* London: Vintage, 2019.

Wyatt, Sir Thomas. *The Complete Poems.* London: Penguin Books, 1997.

Zumthor, Peter. *Atmospheres: Architectural Environments – Surrounding Objects.* Basle: Birkhäuser, 2005.

INDEX